In Quest
of Quasars

In Quest of Quasars

An Introduction to Stars
and Starlike Objects

BEN BOVA

CROWELL-COLLIER PRESS
Collier-Macmillan Limited, London

Once again, to Rosa

The Macmillan Company
Collier-Macmillan Canada Ltd., Toronto, Ontario
Printed in the United States of America

Library of Congress Catalog Card Number: 77-83062

FIRST PRINTING

The lines from "The Secret Sits" are from the
Complete Poems of Robert Frost. Copyright 1942
by Robert Frost. Reprinted by permission of
Holt, Rinehart and Winston, Inc., and Jonathan Cape
Limited, London.

The title page photograph of the Great Galaxy in Andromeda
courtesy of Mount Wilson and Palomar Observatories.

Diagrams by Rosalie Schmidt.

...astronomers...seek to
investigate the true constitution
of the universe — the most
important and most
admirable problem that there is.

—Galileo Galilei

Preface:
The Glorious Quest

THIS BOOK IS ABOUT A PART OF SCIENCE THAT IS USELESS FOR practical purposes—the study of some puzzling lights in the sky called quasars.

Some of the most intelligent men in the world are spending their lives on this study because they are curious and because they may realize that the only lasting thing a man (or a woman) can really add to the world is a new bit of knowledge.

Untold centuries ago, primitive men began wondering about the stars. Eventually this idle curiosity led to calendars and the ability to predict the seasons, which became vitally important when man turned from hunting to farming.

Today the beachheads of science lie in strange places— deep in space, inside the atomic nucleus, down in the molecular structure of living cells. This kind of science, the kind that seeks knowledge for its own sake, is a glorious quest. In a very real sense it is an investment in mankind's future. It is the most human activity man can engage in. But it is even more than that.

It's fun. Nothing can match the thrill of discovering something completely new. And nothing can match the excitement of tackling a problem that has never been faced before.

The study of the quasars has already seen plenty of such thrills and still holds an even greater number of challenges. As for the usefulness of studying quasars?

In the 1830's Michael Faraday (1791–1867) became intrigued with studying electrical and magnetic fields. "What good is it?" he was asked. "What good is a newborn baby?" he replied.

Contents

A cluster of galaxies in the constellation Coma Berenices. Each of the fuzzy objects in the photograph is a galaxy somewhat like our own Milky Way, containing billions of stars (Mount Wilson and Palomar Observatories)

The Discovery
of
the Quasars

**Every so often
in astronomy observational
discoveries burst upon us.**

Geoffrey and Margaret Burbidge

HAVE YOU EVER LOOKED AT THE NIGHT SKY? REALLY LOOKED AT
it: at the beauty of the moon, the stately grandeur of the stars?
The mystery of creation is there, among the stars. Deep in
the heavens lie the answers to our questions of how and when
the universe began, and how it might end.

When you look at the stars, you see a small slice of the
universe. On an exceptionally good night, you can see as
many as two thousand stars and the shimmering band of the
Milky Way arching across the sky.

That is all that any astronomer saw in the heavens, until
1609. In July of that year, the Italian scientist Galileo
Galilei (1564–1642) built a crude telescope and pointed it
toward the stars for the first time. Since then, astronomers
have gone on, using constantly larger and more powerful

telescopes, to probe deeper into space and to push back the borders of the observable universe.

Thanks to their work, we know that the Milky Way is actually a vast pinwheel-shaped island—a galaxy—of some one hundred billion stars; our sun is an average member of this huge family. And the Milky Way is only one out of billions of galaxies. As far as man can see into the heavens, the galaxies go on and on.

And then the quasars were discovered.

Like many of the really important things in the world, quasars did not look impressive—at first glance. Looking like ordinary stars, they can be picked out with a moderately powerful telescope. In fact, quasars were seen and photographed for years without anyone suspecting that they were more than ordinary bluish stars.

What is so unusual about these unimpressive pinpoints of light? Quite a lot:

Quasars may be the most distant objects man has yet seen, out on the edge of the observable universe.

A single quasar may be putting out more energy than a thousand galaxies like the Milky Way.

Quasars may be flying away from us at velocities that approach the ultimate speed limit of the universe: the speed of light, 186,000 miles per second.

Quasars may be doing things that are impossible by everything we know of the laws of physics.

Quasars may be showing us how the universe was created.

Note that we had to say "may be" for each of these statements. No one really knows what the quasars are, or how far away they are, or why they act as they do. That is why they are so exciting. Astronomers are not easily excited. They are accustomed to dealing with mind-boggling ideas and using numbers big enough to make the national debt look paltry. Yet astronomers all over the world were shocked by the discovery of the quasars, and have been more excited over these strange objects than they have been about anything that has happened in many decades. But the bigger and tougher the question, the more there is to be gained from answering it.

The quasar 3C 48 looks like an ordinary star of the sixteenth magnitude in this photograph taken by the 200-inch telescope (Mount Wilson and Palomar Observatories)

RADIO SIGNALS IN THE SKY

The quasars were first detected by radio telescopes. It has been known since 1931 that some celestial objects emit radio waves as well as light. The sun, for example, often flares out with bursts of radio "noise." These radio emissions from space are entirely natural in origin. Actually, light waves and radio waves are the same thing—electromagnetic energy. Radio waves are electromagnetic energy at a long wavelength; a single wavelength can be many feet or even miles long. Visible light, on the other hand, comes in wavelengths so short that hundreds of millions of waves can be packed into the space of an inch.

Radio telescopes, then, do the same thing that optical telescopes do. They gather in electromagnetic energy. But since they work in long wavelengths, the radio telescopes must be large themselves. Radio telescopes are huge antennas, and many of them look like the big radar "dishes" that

Figure 1. How a radio telescope works. Radio waves are focused by the reflector onto the antenna. The receiver changes incoming radio signals into an electric current. Changes in signal strength are recorded on a rotating drum graph

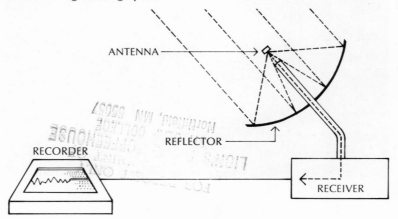

track spacecraft or guard against possible bombing attack. Other radio telescopes consist of long arrays of dipole antennas (something like a rooftop television antenna) that march across the ground for hundreds or thousands of feet.

Astronomers had hoped to be able to find "radio stars." That is, stars that are bright both visibly and in radio emission. Then they could use both types of telescopes to study such stars. In astronomy, as elsewhere, two ways of looking at something usually give much more information than only one. Although all astronomical research was interrupted by World War II, the war did bring about a rapid improvement in electronic equipment. By the 1950's, radio telescopes were springing up all over the world, and the hunt for "radio stars" was on in earnest.

The sun is sometimes a radio star, but it is generally dim in radio output. When a solar flare—a sort of explosion on the sun's surface—occurs, however, a burst of intense radio noise accompanies it. There are other flare stars in the Milky Way, but for the most part all stars are radio-quiet.

On the other hand, there are plenty of things in the sky that put out enormous radio emissions. There is enough free gas floating among the stars of the Milky Way to build another billion or more stars. This gas is mostly hydrogen, and it gives off a radio signal at a wavelength of 21.1 centimeters. Radio astronomers have used this 21 cm. "song of hydrogen" to map out the swirling clouds of interstellar gas, which in turn maps out the spiral arms of our galaxy. The interstellar gas is invisible to optical telescopes, except in the regions where hot, bright stars are close enough to make thick clouds of gas shine brightly.

There are also individual objects in the sky that give off powerful radio signals. Not "radio stars," as was once hoped, however. These sources of radio emission—called *discrete*

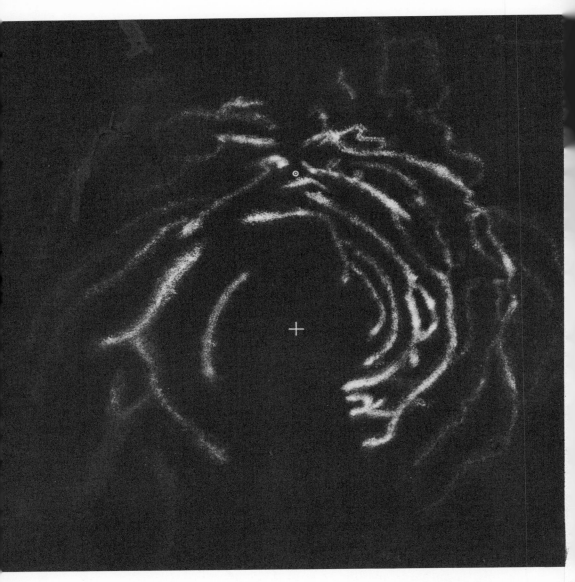

A radio map of the Milky Way. Our solar system is represented by the circled dot, the center of the galaxy by the cross. Radio astronomers mapped clouds of hydrogen gas using 21 cm. wavelength signals to produce this picture. The gap at the bottom of the map is due to shortcomings of the measurement technique (Leiden Observatory, The Netherlands)

sources—are either individual gas clouds or galaxies outside the Milky Way. Or quasars.

Table 1 shows a few of the various types of discrete radio sources, together with the radio output of the entire Milky Way as a reference point.

TABLE 1: POWERFUL RADIO SOURCES

Object	Type	Radio Power
Milky Way	galaxy	1
Crab Nebula (Taurus A)	supernova remnant	0.0001
Cassiopeia A	supernova remnant	0.0001
M 31 (Andromeda Nebula)	galaxy	1
NGC 1068	galaxy	100
M 87	galaxy	10,000
Cygnus A	galaxy	10,000,000
3C 48	quasar	10,000,000
3C 273	quasar	10,000,000

The Crab Nebula (referred to as Taurus A by radio astronomers since it is the "brightest" radio source in the constellation Taurus) is the scene of a supernova explosion that took place on A.D. July 4, 1054. Chinese and Japanese astronomers recorded the event; the supernova was bright enough to be seen in full daylight for nearly a month—without telescopes, of course. Cassiopeia A, although nowhere near as spectacular an object visually, is about as powerful as the Crab Nebula in radio energy. It too is thought to be the remnant of an ancient supernova explosion.

As Table 1 shows, galaxies vary greatly in their radio output. M 31, the beautiful spiral in Andromeda, is considered to be almost a twin of the Milky Way in size, structure, brightness, and radio output. Many other galaxies, though, are much "brighter" in the radio regions of the electromag-

*The Crab Nebula in the constellation Taurus, the remnants of a
supernova explosion in A.D. 1054. This is a powerful radio source,
known as Taurus A to radio astronomers. A pulsar has been detected
and photographed (see page 88) in the heart of the gas cloud (Mount
Wilson and Palomar Observatories)*

netic spectrum. Cygnus A, which is distant and faint optically, emits more than a million times the radio power of either our galaxy or M 31.

And the quasars might be more powerful still.

LOST: SOME "RADIO STARS"

One of the major difficulties in finding "radio stars" was that radio telescopes generally could not locate the discrete sources exactly. In technical terms, the radio telescopes had poor resolving power. The best they could do was to narrow down the location of a particular source to an area of the sky that was a few minutes of arc wide.

With 180° of arc from horizon to horizon, and 60 minutes of arc in each degree, a few minutes of arc seems a small area. But not small enough. Within such an area, large optical telescopes might find many stars. Which one is the radio source? By way of comparison, modern optical telescopes can resolve angles considerably less than one second of arc, which is 1/3600 of a degree. One second of arc is about the size of a twenty-five cent piece, seen from three miles away.

By 1960 several radio astronomy groups were working hard to pinpoint the locations of radio sources well enough for the optical telescopes to pick out the source visually. They were still hoping to find "radio stars." A group at the University of Manchester, in England, compiled a list of two hundred discrete radio sources that were located to within one second of arc.

In December 1960, Thomas Mathews (born 1919) of the California Institute of Technology Radio Observatory and

Allan R. Sandage (born 1926) of the Mount Wilson and Palomar Observatories found that the radio source called 3C 48 was at the same position as a faint bluish star. The astronomical world thought that the first "radio star" had been located at last.

Early in 1963, a group of Australian radio astronomers used clever thinking and hard work to make precise locations for several other "radio stars." Led by Cyril Hazard, the Australians used the moon as a working tool.

As the moon moves in its orbit around the earth, it passes in front of stars and temporarily blots them out from our view. This is called *lunar occultation*. Hazard and his group realized that the moon also occults radio sources: the moon's

The 210-foot radio telescope in the state of New South Wales, Australia, uses the lunar occultation method to determine the positions of quasars (Australian News and Information Bureau)

solid body cuts off radio emission from discrete sources just as it cuts off starlight. They worked out a technique for using this natural event.

As the moon covers a radio source, the radio signal quickly diminishes and then disappears altogether. The reverse happens as the occultation ends. By timing when a radio source begins to fade out, and how quickly it is completely blocked off by the moon, it is possible to tell how large the source is—that is, how big an angular dimension it covers in the sky. Since the moon's position in the sky is known to a high degree of accuracy for every moment of its orbit, it is also possible to work out the precise location of the radio source.

One of the first "radio stars" the Australians looked at in this way was 3C 273. Surprisingly, it turned out to be two sources that were seemingly connected. Maarten Schmidt (born 1929), at Mt. Palomar, quickly found that 3C 273 could be seen visually. In fact, it had shown up on photographs for many years, but no one took it for anything other than a faint blue star. Now, though, Schmidt turned the 200-

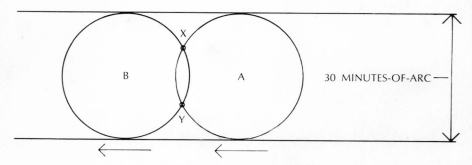

Figure 2. The lunar occultation technique. The quasar disappears when the moon covers it (position A) and reappears when the moon moves far enough to uncover it again (position B). The quasar must then be either at point X or Y. A later measurement, when the moon is in a slightly different position, will show which of the two points is the correct location for the quasar

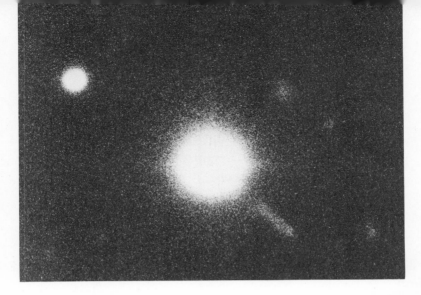

The quasar 3C 273, showing the main body (component B) and the "tail" (component A). Component A emits about 90 percent of the radio energy coming from the quasar (Mount Wilson and Palomar Observatories)

inch telescope on it, and found that 3C 273 did indeed consist of two segments: one small round object, and an elliptical "tail," separated from the starlike object by about 20 seconds-of-arc. The tail, called component A, is much dimmer optically than the round object, component B. But in radio emission, A gives off about 90 percent of the energy emitted by the two components together.

FOUND: THE QUASARS

It was clear by this time that these objects were not "radio stars" after all. Astronomers began to refer to them as "quasistellar objects": objects that are something like stars. Radio astronomers usually called them "quasistellar sources." In 1964 Hong-Yee Chiu (born 1932), a physicist at the NASA Goddard Institute for Space Sciences and a professor at Columbia University, coined the term *quasar*.

With something visible to train their telescopes on, the

optical astronomers began dissecting the light of the quasars. Spectroscopy is an important part of optical astronomy. Visible light consists of a rainbow of colors, all blended together. With a spectroscope, it is possible to "spread out" the light from a star into the distinctive colors of its rainbow-like spectrum. Spectroscopy will be discussed in more detail later in this book. For now, we can simply note that spectroscopy can reveal a star's temperature, chemical composition, rotation rate, and even its speed as it moves through space.

But the spectra of the quasars were puzzling. They seemed to be showing a gas that was highly agitated and very hot. Most puzzling of all was that the chemical composition of the quasars could not be determined. Either they were composed of chemical elements unknown on earth, or they were made of ordinary elements existing under conditions that had never before been seen by the astronomers. Jesse L. Greenstein (born 1909), of the Mount Wilson and Palomar Observatories, suggested that the spectra of the quasars looked something like those produced by hydrogen bomb fireballs.

It was Schmidt who cracked the problem. He assumed that the spectrum of 3C 273 is *redshifted*.

All the galaxies in space, outside of the few closest ones, show redshifted spectra. That is, the light from these galaxies is shifted toward the lower-frequency (red) end of the spectrum, in comparison to light from a known laboratory source. This is interpreted as a Doppler shift, similar to the wail of a train whistle as it shifts toward lower frequencies when it moves away from you. The galaxies, then, appear to be moving away from us.

A fuller discussion of the redshift will be given in Chapter 6. At the moment, we can merely say that all the farther

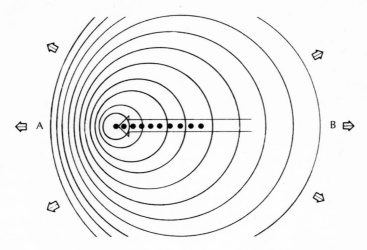

Figure 3. The Doppler shift. The large arrow shows the direction of movement of a source of light waves. The largest circle represents a light wave emitted by the source when it was at the tail of the arrow. The smaller circles represent light waves emitted as the source traveled along the length of the arrow. All the waves are expanding. An observer at point A would see the waves "piled up" and shifted toward the blue, or high frequency, end of the color spectrum. An observer at point B would see the waves "spread out," or shifted toward the red, low frequency end of the spectrum

galaxies are moving away from each other; and the greater their distance, the greater their apparent speed of recession. Since the late 1920's, most astronomers have agreed that the universe is expanding, and this is why the galaxies are moving apart.

If the quasars show redshifts, then they must be at distances comparable to the outermost galaxies. And Schmidt found that the spectrum of 3C 273 could be explained as the spectrum of perfectly ordinary chemical elements redshifted by 16 percent.

Now the full impact of the quasars struck the astronomical world.

MORE SURPRISES

The farthest-known true galaxy has a redshift of some 46 percent and is therefore calculated to be moving away from us at roughly 36 percent the speed of light. While distance values are difficult to pin down, it is estimated that this galaxy is about five billion light years away.

Once Schmidt announced 3C 273's redshift, other quasars were found quickly, with even larger redshifts. Table 2 shows some of them. To date, the farthest objects discovered are several quasars that show redshifts of more than 200 percent, which means they are moving at some 80 percent of the speed of light, and are probably around ten billion light years away. This means that the light we receive from these quasars left them some ten billion years ago. Most estimates for the age of the entire universe are close to ten billion years. Are we seeing, in the quasars, the beginnings of the universe?

That is only the first part of the excitement over the quasars.

Having some idea of their distances, astronomers began to calculate how bright the quasars are. Their real luminosities can be determined from their apparent brightnesses, as we see them from earth, multiplied by their distances.

The numbers are staggering.

The farther quasars seem to be more distant than any known galaxy, yet they are much brighter than galaxies half their distance away. The optical brightness of a typical quasar is equal to one thousand Milky Ways. This means that a single quasar may be shining with the ferocity of *one hundred trillion* stars.

In radio wavelengths the quasars rank with the most powerful radio sources known, as Table 1 shows. A quasar is usually some ten million times "brighter" in radio output than a galaxy of the Milky Way type.

Where does this energy come from? An ordinary galaxy

TABLE 2: QUASAR REDSHIFTS

Quasar	Redshift,%*	Recession Velocity in % of Light Speed	Distance, Light Years (Very Approximate)
3C 273 ✓	16%	15%	2 billion LYs
3C 48	37%	30%	4 billion LYs
3C 295†	46%	36%	5 billion LYs
3C 345	59%	43%	6 billion LYs
3C 446 ✓	140%	70%	9 billion LYs
3C 9 ✓	200%	80%	10 billion LYs

*The technique of measuring redshifts is discussed in Chapter 6.
†3C 295 is not a quasar, but a galaxy; it is the farthest known galaxy.
NOTE: A light year is equal to roughly six trillion miles.

draws on some one hundred billion stars to produce its light and radio output. No one knows, as yet, whether the quasars are groups of stars of about the size of a galaxy or single objects of some wildly unusual sort.

What *is* known is that the quasars seem much smaller in appearance than ordinary galaxies. They appear to be only a fraction of the size that an ordinary galaxy would show at comparable distances. How can they pack all that power into such a small package?

Most amazing of all, the quasars' brightnesses vary. They get brighter and dimmer, some of them over periods as short as a day or a few minutes. They are even "twinkling" in the radio wavelengths. It sounds almost ludicrous, but this twinkling is impossible according to all the known principles of physics.

To explain: one of the cornerstones of physics is that nothing in the universe can move faster than light. There is solid theoretical and experimental evidence to support this belief. If the quasars are distant objects, as their redshifts indicate, they must be large. Not as big as a typical galaxy but large enough so that it would take light waves many years to cross from one end of the quasar to another. As a comparison, a light wave can cross the sun's diameter in five seconds; but it would take some one hundred thousand years for a light wave to cross the diameter of the Milky Way.

The twinkling of the quasars means that something happens to make a quasar get steadily brighter, then steadily dimmer, over and over again. This "something" can happen in only one of two possible ways: either it starts in one spot and spreads across the entire quasar, or every part of the quasar simultaneously brightens and dims, all together.

If it starts in one place and spreads, it cannot go faster than the speed of light. Since some quasars have been observed to brighten up inside of a few days, then they must be small enough for light to cross their whole diameters in a few days. But the quasars seem to be light years, not light days, wide.

Suppose the "something" happens all at once, throughout the length and breadth of the quasar? There is nothing known in science that could happen simultaneously across an object of such size. A few billion stars flaring brighter and dimmer, all in the same rhythm? How? Why?

Either "something" goes faster than light in the quasars or there are things happening in these strange objects that no scientist on earth can even guess at.

Or it may be that the quasars are not at the edge of the known universe after all. Some astronomers have turned to the thought that the quasars might not be as distant as their redshifts would indicate. For the redshift simply means that the object is moving away from us. We interpret this apparent motion as meaning that the universe is expanding, and the quasars—which seem to be moving the fastest—are the farthest objects yet seen.

Other interpretations of the redshifts are possible, as will be seen in Chapter 6. In particular, it is possible that the quasars are relatively nearby, even though they might be moving at high speeds.

The quasars might be comparatively small objects; much larger than a star, but considerably smaller than a galaxy. They might have been shot out of a nearby galaxy, or even blasted out of the Milky Way itself, by some violent action. Something like explosions has taken place in many galaxies.

The advantage of considering the quasars as "local" is that the quasars can be postulated to be much smaller and their fluctuations can be explained more easily. And if the quasars are "local" objects, then their energy is not nearly as great as the "distant" quasar theory estimates it to be. Instead of being more luminous than one thousand galaxies, the quasars might be only one-tenth as bright as an entire galaxy. While this is still equal to the light output of ten billion suns, the energy levels of the quasars are reduced to at least imaginable proportions!

But the "local" quasar theory faces another energy problem: what produced the titanic explosions that hurled the quasars outward from their sources to speeds up to 80 percent of the speed of light?

A chronology at the end of the book briefly sketches the major events in the discovery of the quasars and tells who made the individual observations or theories. At present the arguments for the "distant" and "local" quasar theories are going on in every astronomical center in the world. Both sides can point to serious holes in the other's case. All that either has proved so far is that neither theory can explain the enigmatic and exciting quasars.

2

A Few Words on Jargon

**The urge to know
has evolved from an
instinct into a profession.**

Harlow Shapley

THE PROFESSIONAL SCIENTIST USES A SPECIALIZED, "SHORTHAND" language, jargon. For example, the word *quasar* is a shorthand way of saying "quasi-stellar object," or "quasi-stellar source." Both these longer terms are bits of jargon themselves, and so the word quasar has the distinction of being a shorthand term for a shorthand term! Some other jargon used in the rest of the book follows.

NAMES FOR PEOPLE, PLACES, THINGS

There are several different scientific disciplines involved in the study of quasars. Among them are astronomy, astrophysics, and cosmology.

ASTRONOMY is a general term for the study of the heavens. It includes many different kinds of investigations. In dealing with the quasars, we are most interested in the stars and galaxies, rather than planetary astronomy, which concentrates on our own solar system.

ASTROPHYSICS, as the word indicates, is a combination of astronomy and physics. More specifically, it is usually concerned with studies of the physical nature of the stars. Astrophysics deals principally with nuclear energy, because the stars are gigantic nuclear reactors.

COSMOLOGY is the study of the universe as a whole. Astronomy, astrophysics, and all the other sciences are put to work in cosmological studies, together with a generous dose of philosophy. Cosmology tries to puzzle out the nature of the universe itself, including how and when (if ever) it was created, and how and when it will end.

One of the fine ironies of nature is that man must probe inside the infinitesimal nucleus of the atom to unlock the workings of the infinite heavens. Nuclear energy powers the stars, and we will be discussing some aspects of this in the next few chapters. Nuclear physicists have discovered a host of particles within the atom, but we shall be concerned with only the simplest of them.

ELECTRONS are negatively charged particles. In an ordinary atom, electrons orbit around the nucleus.

PROTONS are positively charged particles, each with a mass 1,837 times greater than the electron. Protons, together with neutrons, make up the atom's nucleus.

NEUTRONS are neutral particles, slightly more massive than protons. In an ordinary atom, neutrons are found in the nucleus. But free neutrons—outside an atom—break down spontaneously in about thirteen minutes to form a proton and electron.

These particles make up atoms. Different atoms, made up of varying amounts of the three basic particles, produce the diverse chemical elements that we know. The hydrogen atom, for example, consists of a single proton as nucleus, and a single electron orbiting around it. Most of the atom is empty space. If the proton were as big as the width of your little finger, the electron would be orbiting about 330 feet away. In between would be nothing—emptiness.

The helium atom, next heaviest among the elements, has two protons and two neutrons in its nucleus, and two orbital electrons. And so it goes, on up to uranium and the even heavier man-made elements, which are more than two hundred times heavier than hydrogen.

Now for a few words about how objects in the heavens get their names.

Of the two-thousand-odd stars that can be seen with the naked eye, only 132 have proper names. The planets have names of their own, and some of the moons circling them have also been given names. (Earth's moon, come to think of it, has no proper name!)

Most of the very bright stars in our sky have proper names—Sirius, Rigel, Polaris. Most of them appear bright to us because they are relatively nearby, not because they are actually more luminous than any of the other stars.

But most other stars are nameless. However, astronomers have devised shorthand terms for identifying them. The star closest to the sun, for example, is usually called Alpha Centauri. This means it is the brightest star in the constellation of Centaurus. Over the years, astronomers have divided the heavens into eighty-eight constellations and tagged the brightest stars in each constellation with Greek letters; the brightest is Alpha, next is Beta, and so forth.

This system works only so far and then breaks down, because large modern telescopes can pick out millions of stars within the boundaries of any constellation. All the alphabets in the world are not enough to give each star an individual designation, although for many years the astronomers tried manfully to keep up with the growing numbers of stars that their constantly better telescopes were revealing. They went through the Greek alphabet, through the Latin alphabet, went back and used double letters, and ultimately gave up. As a result, there are stars named Omicron Orionis, S Doradus, RR Lyrae, and so forth.

Many objects that are not stars are identified by the constellation in which they appear. For example, the great spiral galaxy that is a close twin of the Milky Way, and the nearest large spiral to us, is usually called the spiral galaxy *in Andromeda*. It has no physical connection with Andromeda, and is actually some two million light years away from the stars that make up the constellation. But since the spiral galaxy appears, from our line of sight, within the borders of Andromeda, that is a convenient way to describe what part of the sky it is in.

The great spiral in Andromeda is also known as M 31, which refers to its listing in the Messier catalogue.

In the eighteenth century, the French astronomer Charles Messier (1730–1817) spent many years searching the sky for comets. He found many faint, fuzzy objects that looked as though they might have been comets that were very far from the sun but that later turned out to be other things. Messier published a list of these "not-comets" so that other comet-searchers would not waste their time on them. His catalogue, published in 1784, listed 107 "nebulas." The word nebula means, literally, a cloud. It has been used by astronomers to describe almost any type of object that looks faint and fuzzy. Thirty-four of Messier's "nebulas" are now known to be galaxies. The other objects are either stars, star clusters, or true clouds of interstellar gas.

Other catalogues were put together as the years went on. One of the most useful was first issued in 1895, the New General Catalogue of J. L. E. Dreyer (1852–1926), an Irish astronomer. Many galaxies are identified today by their NGC number.

As radio astronomy became important after World War II, catalogues of radio sources were published. The most widely used of these has been the Third Cambridge Catalogue of Radio Sources, published in 1959 by the radio astronomical group at Cambridge University. This catalogue is known as "3C," and most of the quasars are known by their "3C" numbers.

Of course, the Cambridge astronomers were merely listing the locations of strong radio sources; they had no idea in the late 1950's that such a thing as a quasar existed. There are many other catalogues of radio sources now, including a revised 3C (known as 3C R) and a Fourth Cambridge Catalogue. Whenever you see an object identified by some cryptic initials and numbers, you can be safe in assuming that it is a reference to somebody's catalogue.

NUMBERS FOR DISTANCE, DIMENSIONS, TEMPERATURE

Probably the biggest contribution Galileo made to science was not the telescope nor any of his physical experiments, but his insistence on measurements. Galileo brought the yardstick into science and turned the idle speculations of philosophers into the practical work of physicists. Measurement is the heart of science.

One of the most important types of measurements in astronomy are those of the distances to the stars and galaxies.

It takes light eight minutes to travel from the sun to earth, a distance of roughly 93 million miles. But light needs 4.3 years to go from the sun to Alpha Centauri, the next nearest star. Or put it this way: draw a map in which the 93 million-mile distance from earth to the sun is shrunk to one inch. On that scale, how far away should you place Alpha Centauri? Get a large piece of paper: Alpha Centauri would be 4.3 miles from the sun on such a map.

That's how far the *nearest* star is to the sun.

Alpha Centauri is about 25,222,492,800,000 miles away from the sun. But that is a ridiculously complex way to put it. It is much easier to use a different unit and reduce the numbers. One convenient unit is the light year. Light travels 186,000 miles per second in the vacuum of space. There are about 31.5 million seconds in a year. Therefore light covers a distance of slightly less than six trillion miles in a year. This distance is called a light year. Alpha Centauri, then, is about 4.3 light years away from the sun.

Big as it is, the light year is not the largest "yardstick" used by astronomers. There is the *parsec*, which is equal to 3.262 light years. But as the distances get bigger and bigger, even the parsec becomes dwarfed: astronomers are forced to think in *kiloparsecs* (thousands of parsecs) and *megaparsecs* (millions). These terms will be discussed in Chapter 4.

All scientists prefer the metric system over the clumsy English and American conglomeration of inches, feet, miles, ounces, pounds, and so on. The metric system is based on the number ten, which makes it simple to use. For example, 1500 kilometers is equal to 1,500,000 meters, or 150 million centimeters, or 1.5 billion millimeters.

TABLE 3: METRIC AND ENGLISH UNITS

1 millimeter (mm) = 0.03937 inch

1 centimeter (cm) = 10 mm = 0.3937 inch

1 meter (m) = 100 cm = 39.37 inches,
    or 3.28 feet, or 1.09 yards

1 kilometer (km) = 1000 m = 0.62137 mile

1 mile = 1.6093 km

1 inch = 2.5400 cm = 25.400 mm

1 gram (gm) = 0.0353 ounce = 0.0022046 pound

1 kilogram (kg) = 1000 gm = 2.2046 pounds

1 metric ton = 1000 kg = 2,204.6 pounds

We shall also be using the Kelvin, or absolute, temperature scale for the rest of this book. There are no minus numbers on the Kelvin scale, as Table 4 shows.

TABLE 4: TEMPERATURE SCALES

	°Kelvin	°Centigrade	°Fahrenheit
Water boils	373	100	212
Water freezes	273	0	32
Absolute zero	0	−273	−459

Absolute zero is the temperature at which, theoretically, all molecular motion stops and the energy we call heat would cease to exist. The Kelvin scale starts at absolute zero, which is the lowest possible temperature, and works up. The Centigrade scale uses the freezing point of fresh water as its starting point and employs minus numbers for lower temperatures. The Fahrenheit scale also needs minus numbers.

Note that the Kelvin and Centigrade scales use the same "sized" degrees; there are 100 degrees between the freezing and boiling points of water on both scales. The only difference between them is the position of zero. Thus, in converting from Centigrade to Kelvin you merely add 273; to go from Kelvin to Centigrade, you subtract 273.

The Fahrenheit scale is trickier. To go from Centigrade degrees to Fahrenheit, multiply by 9/5 and then add 32. To go from Fahrenheit to Centigrade, first subtract 32 and then multiply by 5/9.

Most of the shorthand names and number systems have one thing in common: they are simpler, easier, and faster to use than other systems. It might take a little effort to get accustomed to units such as light years, centimeters, and degrees Kelvin, but the result it greater ease in using and understanding astronomical figures.

Another important concept is the "powers-of-ten" number system in which 100 can be written as 10^2, $4000 = 4 \times 10^3$, $7,000,000 = 7 \times 10^6$, and so forth. The superscript refers to the number of zeroes behind the prime number. It also works for numbers smaller than one. For example, $0.1 = 10^{-1}$, $0.01 = 10^{-2}$, $0.000006 = 6 \times 10^{-6}$. The minus superscript indicates how many decimal places are in the number.

Not only does the powers-of-ten notation save writing lots of zeroes, it makes arithmetic much easier. To multiply, you merely add superscripts; to divide, subtract superscripts.

Some practical examples show the utility of this system. How many kilometers are in a light year? The speed of light is roughly 300 billion centimeters per second, and there are 31.5 million seconds in a year, so:

$$(3 \times 10^{10} \text{ cm/sec}) \times (3.15 \times 10^{7} \text{ sec/year}) = 1 \text{ LY}.$$

By multiplying the base numbers (3×3.15) and adding the superscripts we get:

$$1 \text{ LY} = 9.45 \times 10^{17} \text{ cm} = 9.45 \times 10^{12} \text{ km}$$

Light waves are usually measured in Ångstrom units, named after the Swedish physicist Anders Jonas Ångstrom (1814–74). An Ångstrom unit is one ten-millionth of a millimeter: 10^{-7} mm. Visible light lies in the range of about 3,500 to 8,000 Å, or 3.5 to 8×10^{-4} mm.

So much for the ground rules of astronomical jargon. On with the hunt for the quasars!

3
A Star
Among Stars

Thy dawning is beautiful
in the horizon of the sky,
O living Aton, beginning of life.
When thou risest in the eastern horizon,
Thou fillest every land with thy beauty.

The Pharaoh Akhnaton

TO THE ANCIENT EGYPTIANS, THE SUN (ATON) WAS AN OBJECT
of worship. They realized that all life on earth depends on
the sun. Today, we know that all the energy on earth, except
gravitational and nuclear energy, comes from the sun.

The sun is also important in our quest for knowledge about
the quasars. To understand how unique the quasars are and
to get an inkling of what their true nature might be, we
must first examine the stars and galaxies. We must learn
what is known about the heavens before we can approach
what is unknown.

The place to begin is with the sun.

The sun is a fairly typical star, which means that by studying it we can learn a good deal about how stars in general
behave. And the sun is conveniently close at hand for study.

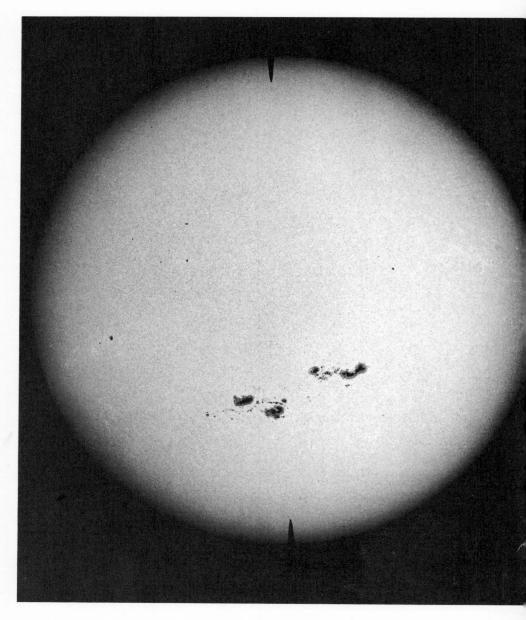

Groups of sunspots on the sun. The marks at the top and bottom of the picture were caused by the telescope's equipment (Mount Wilson and Palomar Observatories)

It is the only star near enough to be seen as a real body. All the other stars are merely pinpoints of light, even in the largest telescopes.

Although the sun may seem placid and friendly, close-up views of its surface show seething turmoil. Bubbling gases, thousands of degrees hot, boil constantly. Huge bolts of glowing gas, big enough to dwarf all the planets of the solar system, are hurled out from the solar surface into space. Giant clouds of gas seem to appear out of nowhere and pour down to the surface like mammoth molten rainstorms. Sunspots usually dot the surface, and intense hot flares flash out from them. Solar flares often affect the earth, buckling our planet's magnetic field, making the aurorae flame far from their usual polar haunts, disrupting long-range radio broadcasts and even scrambling signals on transoceanic telephone cables at the bottom of the sea. In space, the radiation from a solar flare could kill unprotected astronauts in minutes. And the sun, compared to many stars, is quite stable and mild.

Our examination of the sun will begin by looking at how its distance from the earth is measured. This distance measurement is not only critical to understanding the sun, it is important for studies of the whole solar system, the other stars, and the universe at large.

Once distance is known, we can start working out the sun's size, density, and mass. A reliable picture of the sun's physical structure will provide a basis for considering the structures of stars (to be discussed in Chapter 4) and, ultimately, the quasars. We'll pay special attention to the sun's chemical composition, interior structure, and source of energy. The energy source is particularly important. We must know what makes the stars shine before we can tackle the even-more-powerful quasars.

A solar prominence, jets of hot gases at the
sun's surface. The white circle at the right shows
the size of the earth drawn to scale
(Mount Wilson and Palomar Observatories)

The next few pages will attempt to describe not only what is known about the sun, but also how this information was gained.

DISTANCE: A YARDSTICK FOR SPACE

The earth travels around the sun in a not-quite-circular orbit, so that sometimes it is closer to the sun than at other times. The closest point is called *perihelion* (from the Greek words for "near the sun"). Perihelion occurs on January 4 each year. The farthest point, *aphelion* (also Greek: *apo* = away), comes on July 5. We in the northern hemisphere have summer when we are farthest from the sun and winter when we are closest.

Since the earth is not at a fixed distance from the sun, astronomers have settled on an arbitrary value to use as a convenient measure of the earth-to-sun distance. They picked the semimajor axis of the earth's orbit. In simpler terms, it means this: The earth's orbit is elliptical, not circular. As Figure 4 shows, an ellipse has one diameter that is longer than any other. This is called the major diameter, or major

Figure 4. The earth's orbit is not a circle but an ellipse (this drawing shows an exaggerated ellipse). The longest diameter is called the major axis; half of this, the semi-major axis, is defined as the average distance between the sun and the earth, which is called the astronomical unit

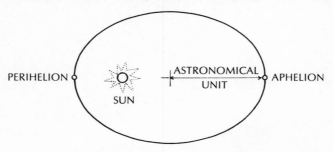

axis. Half that diameter is the semimajor axis. For earth's orbit, the semimajor axis is about 149,598,000 km (or nearly 93×10^6 miles).

This distance is called the *Astronomical Unit* (AU), used to measure some astronomical distances. For example, see Table 5.

TABLE 5: SOLAR SYSTEM DISTANCES

From Sun to:	In 10^6 km	In AU
Mercury	57.9	0.39
Venus	108.2	0.72
Earth (semimajor axis)	149.6	1.00
perihelion	146.4	0.98
aphelion	151.2	1.01
Mars	227.9	1.52
Jupiter	778.3	5.20
Saturn	1428	9.58
Uranus	2872	19.14
Neptune	4498	30.20
Pluto	5910	39.44

The AU is a convenient way of calling out distances in relation to the earth-sun distance. By coincidence, there are about as many AU's in a light year as there are inches in a mile. So you can think of the distances in the solar system as "inches" compared to the "miles" between the stars.

Astronomers have spent a good deal of effort to determine as exact a value as possible for the AU. The most accurate values have come from radar measurements of the distance between the earth and the planet Venus. This sounds strange at first and needs a moment's explanation.

Long before any distances in the solar system were known

in miles or kilometers, astronomers could map out the *relative* sizes of each planet's orbit. Even without a telescope, it is possible to map out the solar system as far as Saturn and show, for example, that Venus's orbit is about two-thirds the size of earth's. Figure 5 shows how this is done.

This kind of map has no scale, no absolute distance values in miles or kilometers. But, if one distance on the map can be measured, then it is possible to fill in all the other distances without further measurements because the map has been drawn to the correct relative scale.

Since the late 1950's, astronomers have teamed with electronics experts in many countries to bounce radar signals off Venus. This has yielded a very accurate value for the distance between the two planets. And these measurements have been turned into a calculation of the AU's value that has an uncertainty of only about 1000 km in it.

Obviously, astronomers would like to make radar measurements of the earth-sun distance directly. But the sun is much farther away, making it necessary to use more powerful equipment, and the return signal is much weaker. Moreover, the sun does not return a radar "echo" as cleanly as a solid planetary body.

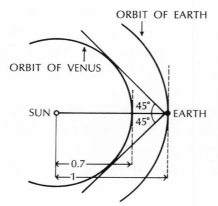

Figure 5. Solar system geometry. The planet Venus never appears farther than 45° away from the sun. The circle centered in the sun and fitting within 45° angles has a radius approximately 0.7 of the radius of the earth's orbit. Thus it is shown that the distance from the sun to Venus averages about 0.7 times the Earth-sun distance

Several other methods have been used to measure the earth-sun distance, but none have been so accurate as the Venus radar measurement. That uncertainty in the AU's value—about 1000 km out of nearly 150 million kilometers—means an accuracy of 99.999 percent.

This may seem to be a great deal of fuss over one distance measurement. But distance measurements are extremely important in astronomy, and the precise value of the AU is vital to all the distance measurements to the stars and beyond. One of the major puzzles of the quasars revolves around the fact that their distances from us are not established well enough to satisfy many astronomers.

HOW BIG IS THE SUN?

With the distance to the sun known, it becomes possible to determine many of the sun's other characteristics.

To start with, the sun presents a disc of about 32 seconds-of-arc (32″) in the sky: about 0.01 of a degree. It looks much larger, mainly because it is so bright; but its angular size is almost exactly the same as the moon's. You can cover either of them entirely with a dime held out at arm's length.

Knowing the distance to the sun, we can convert that angular size into a true measure of the sun's diameter. It works out to 1.39 million kilometers, or 109.3 times the earth's diameter. It would take light five seconds to cross the sun's diameter. The sun's volume is found by $1/6 \ \pi \ D^3$ (where D is the diameter) and equals roughly 2.68×10^{28} km³. That is 268, with 26 zeroes behind it, cubic kilometers. This is more than a million times the volume of earth.

The next step is to determine the mass of the sun. This

is important to understanding the physical nature of the sun itself, and the technique for finding the sun's mass is also used to measure the masses of some stars.

Mass is the amount of matter in an object—your own body, for instance. Here on earth *mass* and *weight* are used as practically interchangeable terms; both are expressed in the same units (gram, kilogram, metric ton).

To find the mass of an object, you measure the gravitational pull it exerts on another body. When you step on a scale to measure your own mass (that is, to weigh yourself), you turn the problem around and measure the pull that the whole earth is exerting on you. The number on the dial would change if you were on the moon. Since the moon's gravitational field is only one-sixth that of earth's, your scale would read one-sixth its terrestrial value. But your mass would not have changed; only the mass of the body you are measuring yourself against has changed.

To measure the masses of celestial objects, you must find two bodies that are close enough to exert a measurable gravitational force on each other. The planets of the solar system are close enough to the sun to allow us to make such measurements.

The simplest thing to do is to measure the sun's gravitational pull on earth. This gravitational attraction accelerates the earth toward the sun. Without the sun's pull, we would go flying off into space; with it, we are bent one-eighth of an inch per second toward the sun. This small amount is what keeps us orbiting around the sun, instead of sailing out of the solar system.

This force can be measured using the principles laid down by Isaac Newton in the seventeenth century. Since the gravitational force exerted by an object is proportional to the object's mass, once we measure the force exerted by the sun, we can calculate its mass.

The sun's mass works out to be about 2×10^{27} metric tons. The earth's mass, which can be measured without astronomical help, is some 6×10^{21} metric tons. The sun, then, is roughly 330,000 times more massive than our far-from-puny planet.

The sun's mass is so great that all the other bodies of the solar system—planets, moons, asteroids, comets, and so forth—make up less than 1 percent of the solar mass.

Yet the sun's density, which is obtained by dividing its mass by its volume, is only 1.41 times the density of water. This is far less than the earth's density of 5.52. This, however, is an average density for the whole sun. The sun's real density varies from practically zero at its outermost layers to several hundred times the density of water deep inside its core.

Now we are ready to look into the structure of the sun. First we will investigate the outer layers, which can be seen with telescopes. Then we will probe into the solar interior, where no telescope can peer. Deep inside the interior, where the sun's energy is produced.

THE OUTER LAYERS

In a sense, we live inside the sun. A constant stream of particles blows out from the sun. Discovered by artificial satellites only ten years ago, this "solar wind" is a stream of protons and electrons that pours past the earth at speeds that range from about 300 to 1600 kilometers per second. Spacecraft have detected the solar wind out to the orbit of

Mars. It probably extends much farther than that, although it might slow down to a "solar breeze" as it wafts by the outer planets.

By terrestrial standards, the space between the shining surface of the sun and the earth's upper atmosphere is an almost perfect vacuum. Typically, there are about ten particles per cubic centimeter in this region of space (protons and electrons, mostly), compared to the 2.45×10^{19} particles per cubic centimeter in the air we breathe.

Looking from the earth toward the sun, we find a series of different regions. First there is the distended, wispy corona; then the rather thin chromosphere; and finally the shining photosphere, which gradually merges into the solid-looking body of the sun. There are no hard-and-fast boundaries between these regions. They are all gases and the differences from one region to another is a matter of degree, not of kind.

The sun's *corona* (which means crown) is a very thin "halo" of gases surrounding the main body of the sun. The corona extends for more than a million kilometers into space and gradually fades into the solar wind that sweeps out past the planets.

Until about 1930, the corona could be seen only during total solar eclipses, when the moon completely covered the sun's luminous body and enabled the feeble light of the corona to be seen from earth. Then Bernard Lyot (born 1897) of France developed the coronagraph, an instrument that fits onto a telescope, blotting out the main disc of the sun much the way the moon does during an eclipse. With the coronagraph, artificial eclipses can be produced on demand.

The temperature of the corona has been found to be about 1,000,000°K, a surprising discovery. This temperature is much

The corona of the sun, photographed during a total eclipse, when the moon blocks out the main body of the sun and allows the faint corona to be seen momentarily (*Mount Wilson and Palomar Observatories*)

higher than the surface temperature of the sun's main body; indeed, it is higher than the surface temperature of any known star. Ordinarily, the surface of the sun ought to be hotter than the outer, thinner layers of gases, if the sun's source of energy comes from inside its core, as astrophysicists feel certain it does. Since heat flows from hot regions to cooler ones, how can the outermost part of the sun have the highest observed temperatures?

The corona has the highest temperature, yes. But it is not the hottest part of the sun's outer layers. High temperature, in a gas as thin as the corona's, does not necessarily mean much heat. The corona gas is of such low density that there is little real material in it. Individual particles in such a thin gas can be accelerated to very high velocities, which we measure as temperature. But because there are so few particles in the gas, it contains little actual heat.

In fact, you would quickly freeze to death in such a "high temperature" gas, if it weren't for the radiant heat coming up from the sun's surface. As we look at other stars and the quasars, we will find more and more cases where high temperatures are produced by something other than ordinary heat. These "non-thermal" energy processes play an important role in studying the quasars.

Moving inward through the corona, we find the layer of gases called the *chromosphere*, or "sphere of color."

Normally the chromosphere is transparent. Like the corona, it could only be seen during a full solar eclipse, and then only briefly as a thin band of reddish light (hence its name). The coronagraph, however, makes the upper region of the chromosphere accessible whenever an astronomer wants to observe it.

This "thin" band of gas is about 8000 km wide, or two-thirds the diameter of earth. When the sun is in full view, of course, the faint light of the chromosphere is drowned out completely by the glare of the solar surface.

There is no sharp boundary between the corona and chromosphere, just as there is no firm line separating the bottom of the chromosphere from the next region of the sun. These different layers merge gradually into one another. The density of the chromosphere increases from that of the lower corona to the density of the sun's "surface." Strangely, the temperature is highest where the chromosphere's density is lowest, near the corona. The temperature decreases closer and closer to the surface. Evidently, the processes that agitate the corona to high temperature are at work in the chromosphere as well.

The innermost layer of solar gases observable from earth is the *photosphere,* or "sphere of light." The photosphere has been called the sun's surface, and the chromosphere is often referred to as the sun's atmosphere. But these terms are misleading. The sun is entirely gaseous; it has no firm surface, and the term atmosphere has no practical meaning, except to denote a layer of gas that sits atop the "surface."

The photosphere is a layer of gas that is slightly transparent, so that you can actually see into it for a depth of about 250 km. Below that level, the gas becomes opaque, and we refer to lower regions as the sun's interior. The density of the photosphere is about 0.01 (10^{-2}) that of sea-level air on earth.

Temperatures in the photosphere vary from about 4500°K at the uppermost level to some 6800°K at the level where it becomes opaque. When astronomers refer to the sun's "surface temperature," however, they are usually referring to a measure of the amount of energy that the sun is putting out, not the actual temperature at a given point in the photosphere. Like the definition of the AU, the definition of the sun's surface temperature is an arbitrary one that the astronomical world has agreed to accept as a useful working concept. It is derived in the following manner.

Each square centimeter on earth receives an estimated 1.92 calories of energy per minute from the sun. That number is based on several assumptions and it is not absolutely accurate; for example, since the cloud-speckled atmosphere of earth absorbs solar energy in a nonuniform way, the 1.92 calorie/cm²/min is the amount of energy estimated to be received at the top of the atmosphere. This is called the *solar constant*: the amount of energy the earth receives from the sun. A calorie is the amount of energy that will raise the temperature of a gram of water one degree centigrade (or Kelvin). The calories listed in diet and nutritional writing are actually *kilocalories,* one thousand calories each.

If we know how much energy the earth is receiving from the sun and how far away the sun is, we can calculate how much energy the sun is emitting. This comes from the simple fact that electromagnetic energy obeys the *inverse-square law*: for increase in distance, the intensity of the energy decreases by the square of the distance. For example, take a row of streetlights. Call the brightness of the nearest light $B = 1$. The next light is twice as far away as the first one; the distance, D, is $D = 2$. The brightness of this second light is then $B = 1/D^2$, or $B = 1/(2)^2$, or $B = 1/4$. A light that's three times away has a brightness of $1/9$; five times away, $B = 1/25$. The inverse square law is a powerful tool, especially when examining distant stars and galaxies.

Since all electromagnetic radiation (and gravity, too, for that matter) obeys the inverse square law, we can calculate that a solar constant on earth of 1.92 calories/cm²/min

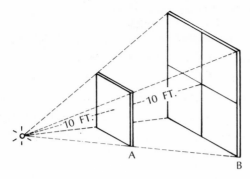

Figure 6. The inverse square law. Doubling the distance from the light source cuts the amount of light received to one-fourth. To an observer at point B, the light would be only one-fourth as bright as it is to an observer at point A. The inverse square law holds true for all electromagnetic radiation and for gravity

means that each square centimeter of the sun's surface must be beaming out 1500 calories per second. This equates to a temperature of 5750°K, which is usually rounded off to 6000°K and given as the surface temperature of the sun.

The numbers are rather dry, by themselves. In *Exploration of the Universe*, George Abell gives a dramatic example of how much heat we are talking about:

> [Imagine] a bridge of ice 2 miles wide and 1 mile thick, and extending over the nearly 100-million-mile span from the earth to the sun. If all the sun's radiation [energy] could be directed along that bridge, it would be enough to melt the entire column of ice in one second.

With a surface temperature that high, every element in the photosphere must be completely vaporized and in gaseous form. Carrying out this line of attack, we can reason that if the photosphere is gaseous, the interior of the sun must be, too.

The fact that the sun shines, that energy is being radiated away from its surface, shows that the energy is most likely being produced below the surface. In the photosphere and the sun's interior, we are dealing with gas densities where temperature and heat can be equated. So if the sun is radiating energy away from its surface, we have strong reasons to suspect that the interior is hotter and therefore gaseous.

In summary, as we look in toward the sun from earth we see first the corona, then the chromosphere, and finally the photosphere. Each region blends gradually into the next. All are composed of hot (or at least high-temperature) gases; the gas density steadily increases as we go deeper, until finally the gas becomes opaque and we can see no farther. We deduce that the interior of the sun is also gaseous, although no doubt more dense than the photosphere, and certainly hotter.

FINGERPRINTS FROM RAINBOWS

Before discussing the interior of the sun, we must cover spectroscopy, a scientific "fingerprinting" technique that allows astrophysicists to determine the chemical elements present in the sun's gases.

Light from the sun, or from any natural or artificial source, can be broken up into a *spectrum* of separate colors as raindrops sometimes break up sunlight into a rainbow. Astronomers use glass prisms or diffraction gratings to "spread out" the light of the sun and stars into their spectra.

In Germany in 1859, the physicist Gustav Kirchhoff (1824–87) and the chemist Robert Bunsen (1811–99) uncovered the laws that govern this behavior of light. They found that a dense object, such as the sun's main body or a piece of metal heated until it is glowing, gives off a rainbow-like blend of many colors. This is called a *continuous spectrum*.

When ordinary light is passed through a fairly thin gas, however, dark lines show up in the otherwise continuous spectrum. These lines are caused by atoms or molecules of the gas. Different elements in the gas absorb different wavelengths of light and produce dark absorption lines at specific places along the spectrum. Each chemical element produces its own characteristic set of absorption lines, as unique as fingerprints. Thus it is possible to identify the elements in a gas, no matter where it is in the universe, if the gas is under conditions that produce an *absorption spectrum*.

The sun's photosphere is a region of fairly thin gas sitting atop a dense, bright light source. The sun therefore shows a continuous spectrum that is crossed by some six hundred dark absorption lines. The German physicist Joseph Fraunhofer (1787–1826) made one of the earliest studies of these lines in 1814, and they are called Fraunhofer lines to this day.

Scientists have produced absorption spectra in the laboratory from known elements and catalogued the wavelengths at which each element produces absorption lines. By comparing the positions of the absorption lines in the sun's spectrum with these known laboratory spectra, astrophysicists have been able to identify more than sixty elements in the sun's photosphere. Any single element will produce more than one absorption line, so there is no one-to-one matching between the number of absorption lines in a spectrum and the number of elements present in the light source.

Helium was first recognized as a new element in the sun's spectrum before it was discovered to exist on earth; hence its name, *helios* = sun. The corona's spectrum showed certain lines that could not be identified with any known terrestrial element, and for a while the name *coronium* was used. But

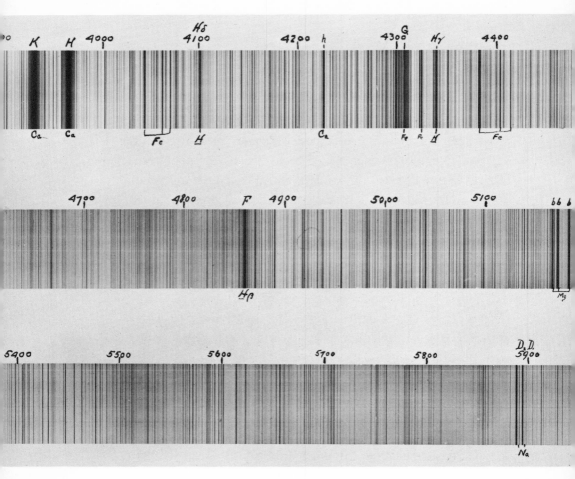

A portion of the sun's spectrum as taken with a spectroheliograph (Mount Wilson and Palomar Observatories)

later it was learned that coronium is actually iron under very unusual conditions, so that it put out spectral lines that were not at first recognized because they did not match laboratory spectra. Now the corona is sometimes called "the sun's iron crown."

Spectral analysis can also detect compounds as well as pure elements. Compounds are molecules made up of the atoms of different elements: for example, water (H_2O), ammonia (NH_3), methane (CH_4).

Because of spectroscopy, we know that the photosphere of the sun is composed almost entirely of hydrogen and helium, with less than 1 percent of heavier elements. The ratio of hydrogen to helium is less certain; estimates vary from nearly 50 percent hydrogen to 98 percent hydrogen (by mass). Table 6 shows how the abundances of elements in the sun matches the abundances found elsewhere in the heavens.

Kirchhoff and Bunsen also found that under certain conditions a gas will emit bright lines of color in an otherwise

---

TABLE 6: ABUNDANCES OF ELEMENTS

Element	Universe	Earth	Crust
H (Hydrogen)	3.5×10^8	—	1,400
He (Helium)	1.4×10^7	—	—
C (Carbon)	38,000	—	27
N (Nitrogen)	83,000	—	3
O (Oxygen)	140,000	38,000	29,500
Ne (Neon)	160,000	—	—
Na (Sodium)	490	130	1,250
Mg (Magnesium)	11,000	15,000	870
Al (Aluminum)	870	350	3,050
Si (Silicon)	10,000	10,000	10,000
S (Sulfur)	4,300	1,800	—
K (Potassium)	66	40	670
Ca (Calcium)	690	330	920
Ti (Titanium)	26	18	133
Fe (Iron)	5,400	13,500	910
Ni (Nickel)	380	1,000	—

The abundances of the elements in the universe at large, in the earth as a whole, and in the earth's crust. The number of silicon atoms is arbitrarily set at ten thousand in all cases, and the values for the other elements computed accordingly. Note that the universe is almost entirely hydrogen and helium, with all the other elements forming a small percentage of "impurity," while the earth is mostly "impurity" (after Brian Mason).

dark spectrum. The sun's chromosphere and corona do this. Apparently these gases are absorbing energy from the photosphere beneath them and then re-emitting some of the energy in wavelengths of light that are characteristic of the gases present in these layers.

Here, too, the gases are almost entirely hydrogen and helium. Spectroscopic studies have revealed that the stars and interstellar gases, as Table 6 shows, are also composed mainly of these two lightest elements. In fact, the sun's lonely percent or so of heavier elements is considerably more than many stars show. The entire universe—including the quasars, apparently—is almost entirely hydrogen and helium, with a smattering of heavier elements.

FROM THE SURFACE INWARD

Just as we deduced that the sun's interior must be hotter than its surface, we might assume that the interior is also composed mainly of hydrogen and helium. Theoretical considerations, derived from a "model" of the sun that can account for its observed size, mass, density, and luminosity, give strong weight to the conclusion that the sun must be composed of these two lightest elements.

Think a moment about how conditions must change as you go down deeper from the photosphere toward the sun's center. The deeper you go, the denser the gas. This is due to the weight of billions upon billions of tons of matter, all pressing downward toward the core. Why doesn't the sun collapse? How can it stay gaseous throughout, when the weight of its own matter should be trying to squeeze it down into a much smaller, more solid ball? Calculations based on the sun's known gravitational forces show these forces *should* pull the sun into a small sphere of enormous density.

Obviously, those calculations are leaving out something important. Something is balancing this inward-pulling force of gravity, something is pushing outward from the sun's core.

At the core of the sun, the gas density must be several hundred times that of water, far more than the density of any of the planets, including our iron-cored earth. Under these conditions, the gas temperature must be extremely high, since temperature normally rises in proportion to density.

Astrophysicists have calculated that the temperature of the sun's center must be in the neighborhood of twenty million degrees Kelvin. If this is correct, it would explain how the sun remains gaseous throughout despite its interior density: no material could be anything but gaseous at that temperature, no matter what the density.

At that temperature, the gas pressure must be enormous, since the pressure in a gas is proportional to the temperature. It is probably as high as a billion times the pressure of sea-level air here on earth. This gas pressure is an outward-pushing force, just as the air you blow into a paper bag pushes out its sides. And it is gas pressure that helps to balance the inward-pulling force of gravity and to keep the sun at a constant spherical size.

Now we must take a deeper look at the composition of the sun and correct an oversimplification. The sun is almost entirely composed of hydrogen and helium, and, we have learned, it is gaseous throughout.

Actually, the sun is not composed of gas. It is made of *plasma*, which though very much like a gas is quite different. Physicists have called plasma the fourth state of matter: solid, liquid, gas, and plasma.

In a plasma some of the electrons that are usually locked in orbit around the gas atoms have been knocked loose, so that they are free to move as independent particles. This means that a plasma can conduct electrical currents; gases cannot do this.

In addition to having all the behavior traits of ordinary gases, plasmas can be affected by electromagnetic forces. Electrical currents can flow in a plasma. This means that magnetic fields will permeate the plasma, because moving electrical charges create magnetic fields. Plasmas can be shaped, heated, moved by electrical and magnetic forces. Moreover, there are enormous energies locked up in plasmas. It takes energy to remove electrons from atoms, and that energy is stored in the plasma, available for use.

In a plasma, then, there can be three main types of particles: *neutral atoms*, which have not lost any electrons; *free electrons*, which have been removed from once-neutral atoms; and *ions*, which are what is left of an atom after it has lost one or more electrons. The electrons carry a negative electrical charge, and the ions have a net positive charge, since they have lost electrons. The neutral atoms, of course, are electrically neutral; their positive and negative charges are in balance.

Although the plasma can conduct electricity, it is itself electrically neutral on the whole since for every free electron there is a balancing positively charged ion from which it came. Plasmas are also called *ionized gases*, since a plasma is a gas that has been ionized. The word "plasma" was coined by the American Nobel Laureate Irving Langmuir (1881–1957), who recognized the distinct properties of ionized gases during experiments he conducted in the early 1900's.

The sun is plasma throughout, from core to solar wind. All the stars are plasma, and large amounts of the clouds of gases that have been seen in interstellar space are ionized. Most of the universe is plasma! Only in tiny, cold places like the planet earth do the low-energy states of matter—solids, liquids, and gases—exist. Quasars are plasma.

Plasmas are seldom found on earth. Lightning strokes create a plasma around themselves for a flash of a second; so do man-made electrical discharges, such as Langmuir was studying when he coined the term. Fluorescent lamps are filled with gases that become ionized when you switch them on so that an electrical current runs through them. And the energetic exhaust blasting out of rocket nozzles is plasma.

Calculations show that at the sun's core the plasma is completely ionized. At a temperature of some twenty million degrees, there are no neutral atoms. Every atomic nucleus is completely stripped of orbital electrons, and the plasma consists of bare nuclei and free electrons.

THE SUN'S SOURCE OF ENERGY

A million-kilometer-wide ball of hydrogen and helium, with an interior temperature of 2×10^7 °K has an amazingly large amount of energy in it. How is this energy converted into sunshine?

Apparently, the sun has been glowing steadily for billions of years. Geologists have found that the earth is about four and a half billion years old. Meteorites are also about the same age. The entire solar family was probably formed some five billion years ago. And the sun must be at least that old.

Paleontologists have traced life on earth back at least two billion years. If the sun's radiation had changed drastically during that time, all life might well have been wiped out. The fact that the oceans have not been boiled away or frozen completely shows that the earth's temperature has remained within a fairly narrow range—only one hundred degrees separate boiling from freezing. Thus the sun must have been almost perfectly constant in heat output for billions of years.

What is the source of this unfailing energy? When scientists first began to realize, in the latter half of the nineteenth century, that the sun is billions of years old, this question became crucially important. The sun pours out some 3.8×10^{33} ergs per second, which is the energy equivalent of more than 10^{10} megatons of TNT exploded *every second*. This has gone on for billions of years!

In the nineteenth century, nothing known to man could account for this fantastic energy production. If the sun were a mixture of pure carbon and oxygen, for example, and burned like a coal flame, it would have burned itself out within a few thousand years. Several astronomers considered that the sun might be slowly shrinking and converting gravitational energy into heat energy. But calculations show that this energy source would last only a few million years.

By the 1930's physicists were excitedly probing the nucleus of the atom and finding enormous energies there. In 1938, Hans Bethe (born 1906), who had come to America from Germany, and Carl F. von Weizsacker (born 1912), in Germany, both worked out the basic principles of nuclear energy production in the sun. Neither man knew of the other's work at that time. Bethe received the Nobel Prize in physics in 1967 for this work.

The principle of nuclear energy is summed up by Einstein's equation, $E = mc^2$. That is, energy can be produced from matter. Under proper conditions, matter can be converted into energy and vice versa; in fact, matter and energy are fundamentally the same thing.

TABLE 7: HYDROGEN FUSION PROCESSES

Carbon Chain

$$H^1 + C^{12} \rightarrow N^{13} + \gamma$$
$$N^{13} \rightarrow C^{13} + e^+ + \nu$$
$$C^{13} + H^1 \rightarrow N^{14} + \gamma$$
$$N^{14} + H^1 \rightarrow O^{15} + \gamma$$
$$O^{15} \rightarrow N^{15} + e^+ + \nu$$
$$N^{15} + H^1 \rightarrow C^{12} + He^4$$

Proton-Proton Reaction

$$H^1 + H^1 \rightarrow H^2 + e + \nu$$
$$H^2 + H^1 \rightarrow He^3 + \gamma$$
$$He^3 + He^3 \rightarrow He^4 + 2H^1$$

Key

H^1 = Hydrogen (proton)
H^2 = Deuterium (deuteron)
He^3, He^4 = Helium isotopes
C^{12}, C^{13} = Carbon isotopes
N^{13}, N^{14} = Nitrogen isotopes
O^{15} = Oxygen isotope
e^+ = positron (positive electron)
γ = gamma ray
ν = neutrino

Two nuclear fusion processes for converting hydrogen to helium, releasing energy in the form of gamma rays and neutrinos. Note that in the carbon chain, only four hydrogen nuclei (protons) and one carbon nucleus are required as input; the carbon nucleus, after several transmutations, returns to its original form at the chain's end. In the sun, the proton-proton reaction produces most of the energy. Carbon chain reactions are more important in hotter stars.

Here on earth, the two seem quite separate and distinct. Matter is one thing and energy is another. But our planet is only a tiny chunk of solids, liquids, and gases; it is not representative of the entire universe.

At the core of the sun, where temperatures reach twenty million degrees or more, nuclear fusion reactions that change matter into energy can easily take place: the plasma there is completely ionized. There are no neutral atoms, they have been broken up into bare nuclei and free electrons. As Table 7 shows, four hydrogen nuclei (single protons) engage in reactions that eventually produce a helium nucleus (two neutrons and two protons). The helium nucleus is 0.7 percent lighter than the original mass of the four hydrogen nuclei. This amount of mass is converted into energy, energy we receive here on earth as sunshine and, occasionally, as radio waves.

Although 0.7 percent may seem like a small amount of mass to account for the sun's enormous energy output, it means that the sun is converting about four million tons of matter into energy every second. The sun has been shedding mass at this rate for billions of years. Yet, if all the hydrogen in the sun were converted to helium, the sun would be only 0.7 percent lighter than if it were pure hydrogen.

The sun, then, is a controlled *thermonuclear* reactor. It produces energy in much the same way that an H-bomb produces an explosion: through nuclear fusion. But the sun does it in a controlled and continuous manner.

This raises several important points. First, the energy produced by the sun can be thought of as four million tons of radiation per second. Radiation can exert pressure, and the radiation produced inside the sun is an outward-pushing force, just like the gas pressure (although much weaker). Radiation pressure helps gas pressure to fight against gravity in the sun. In hotter, more luminous stars, radiation pressure plays an important role in maintaining the star's equilibrium against gravitational collapse.

Second, if the sun is continuously converting hydrogen into helium, then its helium content is growing as time goes on. Was the sun all hydrogen originally? Third, more important to us, what will happen when the sun runs out of hydrogen?

THE SUN AS A STAR

If the sun is a typical star, then nuclear energy must be the source of starlight. Although the stars may have life-spans that are measured in billions of years, if they depend on a nuclear "fuel" such as hydrogen, then they must change radically or perhaps die out completely when their fuel is used up.

Radio astronomers have found that the sun often emits strong bursts of radio frequency energy. These are usually associated with the eruption of solar flares.

The causes of flares are not fully known. They are connected with sunspots, mainly a mystery, vast islands of plasma sitting at the bottom of the photosphere. They appear dark because they are slightly cooler than the surrounding photosphere. But, as Galileo showed, sunspots are actually hot and bright. We know that plasmas are usually found linked with magnetic fields, and there are intense magnetic fields around the sunspots. Most astrophysicists feel that the magnetic fields in the photosphere and outer layers actually carry energy to the chromosphere and corona, thereby raising their temperatures to the high levels found there. But the exact mechanism for transferring their energy through the magnetic fields is still unknown. Undoubtedly, the magnetic fields also play a powerful role in the production of flares and radio bursts.

However, the type of radio activity that the sun produces cannot explain the tremendous radio energies received from the quasars. The quasars' radio output is not explained by assuming that they are giant collections of sunlike stars.

Although the sun is a fairly typical star, there are many other kinds of stars in the Milky Way galaxy as well as many other types of galaxies.

4

Stars of All Descriptions

There is one glory of the sun,
and another glory of the moon,
and another glory of the stars;
for star differs from star in glory.

I Corinthians 15:41

THE SUN IS SUPPOSEDLY AN AVERAGE STAR. STARS IN GENERAL vary a great deal: there are the average and unusual, the giants and dwarfs, stars of all colors, all brightnesses, all descriptions.

Before we can hope to understand the quasars, if the quasars are a peculiar type of star, we need to know as much as possible about stars. If the quasars are more like galaxies, each quasar may contain billions of stars.

About fifty years ago, Ejnar Hertzsprung (born 1873) in the Netherlands and Henry Norris Russell (1877–1957) in the United States developed a way to compare various stars (see the diagram on page 60). As often happens in science, the two men worked independently of each other; neither knew that the other had hit upon the same idea.

The *Hertzsprung-Russell diagram* has nothing to do with the stars' positions in the sky. It is not a map to locate and identify the stars or constellations in the night sky.

It *is* a way of showing some important physical features of the stars. The stars are plotted on the H-R diagram according to two characteristics: brightness and color.

Figure 7 is an H-R diagram for the twenty brightest stars in the sky, plus the sun, as seen from the earth. If twenty thousand stars—or twenty million—were plotted in this way, the main features of the illustration would still tend to show up. Unless an unusual group of stars is being plotted, every H-R diagram tends to show a strong grouping of stars along the diagonal line called the *main sequence*. And there are usually separate groupings in the areas labeled Red Giants and Supergiants, and White Dwarfs.

If such groupings tend to show up in samplings of millions of stars the conclusion is that there must be some physical reasons for this. Although the stars come in a wide variety of sizes, colors, and brightnesses, this variety is not random, not haphazard. Physical principles govern the behavior of the stars, and physical principles can be observed and understood.

When astronomers study a star, all they have to work with —even when using the largest telescopes—is a pinpoint of light. When a star is photographed, its light builds up on the film and spreads the image enough to make it look as though the star is showing a disc; but this is strictly an artifact caused by the limitations of photographic film. From the points of light, astronomers try to determine the present conditions and life histories of the stars. We can try to do the same for the twenty brightest stars of the illustration.

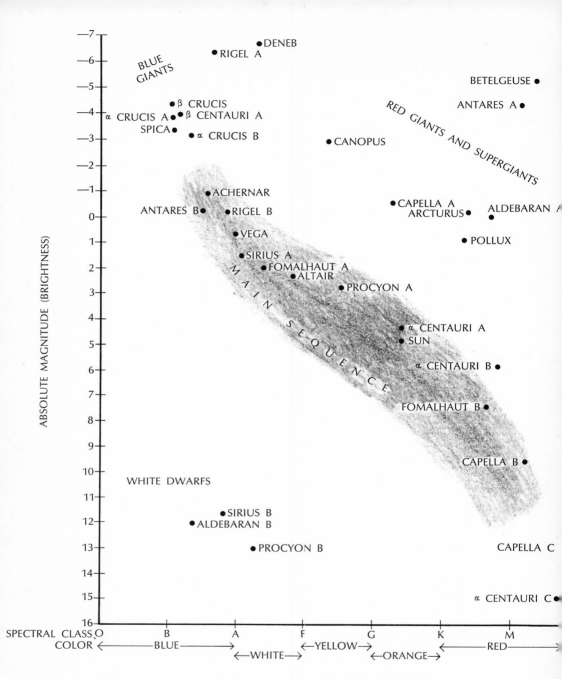

Figure 7. A Hertzsprung-Russell diagram for the twenty brightest stars, plus the sun, in the sky as seen from the earth. The diagram plots the relationship between spectral class (color) of the stars and their brightnesses

BRIGHTNESS AND COLOR

Table 8 lists the twenty brightest stars and the sun as seen from the earth. The term *apparent magnitude* refers to how bright a star looks from earth. This system of magnitudes dates back to Hipparchus, a Greek astronomer of the second century B.C.

TABLE 8: THE TWENTY BRIGHTEST STARS

Name	Apparent Magnitude*	Color*
SUN	−26.5	yellowish
1. Sirius A + B	−1.42	blue-white
2. Canopus	−0.72	yellow-white
3. Alpha Centauri A + B + C	−0.01	yellowish
4. Arcturus	−0.06	orange-red
5. Vega	+0.04	white
6. Capella A + B + C	0.05	yellow
7. Rigel A + B	0.14	blue
8. Procyon A + B	0.38	yellow-white
9. Betelgeuse	0.41	red
10. Achernar	0.51	blue
11. Beta Centauri A + B	0.63	blue
12. Altair	0.77	white
13. Aldebaran A + B	0.86	orange
14. Spica	0.91	blue
15. Antares A + B	0.92	red
16. Pollux	1.16	orange
17. Fomalhaut A + B	1.19	white
18. Deneb	1.26	blue-white
19. Beta Crucis	1.28	blue
20. Alpha Crucis A + B	1.39	blue

Value given for A component of multiple stars.

For each step in magnitude, brightness changes by a factor of 2.512. Therefore a difference of five magnitudes equals a difference of 100 in brightness. This is a *geometric progression,* where each step forward is 2.512 bigger than the preceding step. The geometric progression is a powerful tool for handling rapidly increasing numbers. You need only five steps to go from 1 to 100 in brightness; only 20 steps to go from 1 to 100 million.

One tricky point about magnitudes is that there are minus numbers assigned to the very brightest stars. Figure 8 should help to clarify matters. The minus numbers got into the system for reasons of history, not physics. Brightnesses *decrease* as the plus numbers get larger, but *increase* with larger minus numbers.

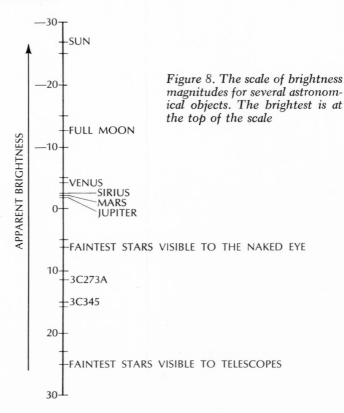

Figure 8. *The scale of brightness magnitudes for several astronomical objects. The brightest is at the top of the scale*

As the illustration shows, the quasars are far from the dimmest objects visible to modern telescopes, although they may be the farthest objects man has seen. The two-hundred-inch telescope at Mt. Palomar can photograph objects down to about 23d magnitude (m = 23). In the near future, this telescope will be fitted with electronic image-intensifying equipment, so that it will be able to photograph even fainter objects. Several telescopes around the world have already received electronic "boosters"; until telescopes are in orbit or on the moon, this method seems the most promising way of getting more information with optical equipment.

The apparent magnitudes of some of the brightest quasars are shown in Table 9.

TABLE 9: THE BRIGHTEST QUASARS

Quasar	Apparent Magnitude (m)
3C 273	
A component	12.8
B component	19
PKS 2135-14	15.53
3C 249.1	15.72
3C 48	16.2
3C 345	16.8

Some of the stars listed in Table 8 are more than single objects. Alpha Centauri is a triple star. Sirius and Procyon are both binaries. Many quasars are double objects, too; 3C 273 is an outstanding example.

Table 8 also lists the colors of the twenty brightest stars. Just as in an ordinary flame, colors toward the blue end of the spectrum indicate higher temperatures than do reddish colors. Through spectrographic analysis of the light from a star, it is possible to determine surface temperature, chemical composition, and many other important characteristics of a star. Astronomers have a system for classifying stellar spectra; the majority of stars fall into seven main spectral categories, as shown in Table 10.

TABLE 10: STELLAR SPECTRAL CLASSES

Spectral Class	Surface Temperature (°K)	Color	Examples
O	above 25,000	blue-violet	rare
B	11,000–25,000	blue	Rigel, Spica
A	7500–11,000	blue, blue-white	Sirius, Vega
F	6000–7500	blue-white, white	Canopus, Procyon
G	5000–6000	white, yellow	Sun, Capella, Alpha Centauri A
K	3500–5000	orange, red	Arcturus, Aldebaran, Alpha Centauri B
M	less than 3500	red	Betelgeuse, Antares, Alpha Centauri C

Although our knowledge of the quasars is far from complete, it is known that they are intrinsically intensely blue objects—in fact, they probably emit some of their radiation in ultraviolet wavelengths, which would be unobservable on earth. Their radiation is visible mainly because it has been redshifted down from the UV wavelengths to the blue, where it can penetrate the earth's atmosphere. The temperature of the plasma that produces this radiation has been estimated to be around 30,000°K or more; somewhat above that of the O-class stars.

Originally, the sequence of spectral classifications started with A and went on in alphabetical order. But refinements and corrections over the years have scrambled the sequence to the point where astronomy students must memorize, "Oh, be a fine girl, kiss me!" to remember the proper order of spectral classes.

Each spectral class is divided into ten subgroups. The sun and Alpha Centauri A are both G2 stars, for example, while the slightly hotter Capella A is G0, Betelgeuse is M2, and Alpha Centauri C is M5, and so on.

So far we have considered only how the stars look from earth. A star's apparent magnitude depends on (1) its actual luminosity, that is, the amount of light it is actually emitting; and (2) its distance from earth.

Recalling the inverse-square law from the previous chapter: the farther a star is from earth, the dimmer its light will appear; the brightness is inversely proportional to the square of the distance. The sun has an enormous apparent magnitude, m = −26.5. Does this mean that the sun is truly the brightest of all the stars? Hardly. The sun is only "an inch" away from us, compared to the "miles" of distance to the other stars.

To learn what the stars are really like, we must somehow get to see them as they really are, and not as they happen to appear from our particular observation platform. Astronomers use the term *absolute magnitude* to refer to the true brightness of a star, irrespective of its distance. Absolute magnitude is usually denoted by a capital M, as opposed to the lowercase m used for apparent magnitude.

But to find the absolute magnitudes of the stars, we must cancel out the effect of their distances. And before we can do this, we must know what those distances are. Distance measurements over the spans of light years are extremely important, and they are extremely difficult to make.

PARALLAX: THE MILES-LONG TRIANGLE

George Washington knew how to measure the distance to an object he couldn't touch. As a part-time surveyor, he was quite familiar with the technique of triangulation measurements.

If he wanted to measure the width of a river, he would start by laying out a baseline along the shore, using a chain or line that was already measured in length. Next he would pick out a target on the opposite side of the river—say, a tree growing right along the bank. From each end of the baseline, he would sight the target tree and measure the angles formed between the target and the ends of the baseline. The longer the baseline, the larger the angles and the easier the measurement.

He would then have a triangle in which he knew the length of the base and the sizes of the two base angles. A glance at a trigonometry table would enable him to work out the distance between the tree and the baseline.

Astronomers also use trigonometric triangulation measurements when seeking the distance to a star. But because the stars are so far away, they need a gigantic baseline; otherwise the angles they are trying to measure are too small to work with. The whole earth is not big enough to hold a baseline that can be used on even the nearest stars, so astronomers have turned to a baseline that is literally out of this world: the three-hundred-million-kilometer-long diameter of the earth's orbit around the sun.

The astronomer will photograph the star he's working on and wait six months for the earth to swing around to the other end of his baseline. Then he photographs the star again, usually on the same plate. Often the astronomer will photograph the star at least once more, so the job usually takes a year or more.

If all goes well, the photographic plate will show at least two different images for the target star. There will also be many background stars in the picture, but their images should overlap, since they are farther away than the target star and show no shift in position. This shift of the target star is called its *parallax* (see Figure 9).

You can demonstrate a parallactic shift by holding your thumb out at arm's length and squinting at it with one eye at a time. As you switch from one eye to another, your thumb will seem to move across the background against which you

Figure 9. The parallactic shift technique for determining a star's distance. The position of the star is measured against the positions of fainter background stars, then measured again six months later, when the earth is at the opposite end of its 300-million-kilometer-wide orbit around the sun. The apparent shift in the star's position allows astronomers to determine its distance from the sun

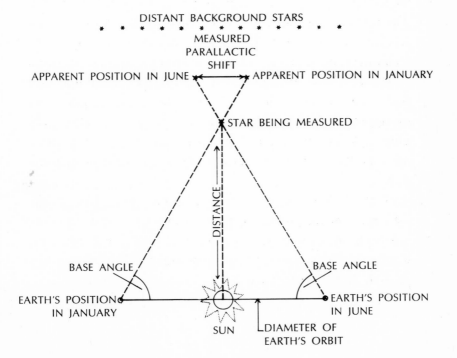

are viewing it. But the shift your thumb shows is huge compared to the parallactic shifts that astronomers get from the stars.

The largest parallactic shift that has been seen for any star is only 0.76 seconds-of-arc (abbreviated as 0.″76), for Alpha Centauri. You recall that one second-of-arc is about the size of a twenty-five-cent piece seen three miles away.

The term *parsec* is used by astronomers as a unit of distance. This word is formed by combining *par*allax and *sec*ond-of-arc. One parsec is the distance an object would be at if it showed a parallax of 1″. This distance equates with 3.26 light years. No star has been discovered this close to us; Alpha Centauri is 1.3 parsecs or 4.3 light years away. Many astronomers prefer to express distances in parsecs, because they feel that the term light year often confuses nonastronomers and sounds too romantic.

Because parallactic shifts are so small, reliable triangulation measurements have been made for only a few hundred stars. The technique gives good results down to a parallax of about 0.″05—a distance of twenty parsecs. Beyond that range, other techniques must be used, such as comparing the apparent magnitude of an unknown star against the magnitude of a star whose distance has been measured, counting on the inverse-square law to get the distance to the new star. Such indirect techniques are not as reliable as triangulation methods, but they are all that can be done for the vast majority of stars.

Once the distance to a star is known, even though the measurement may be indirect and subject to some error, we can begin to see what it is really like. Table 11 lists the same stars as given in Table 8, but now they are ranked in order of their true luminosities.

TABLE 11: PHYSICAL DATA FOR THE BRIGHTEST STARS (Ranked by Luminosity of A Component)

NAME	Distance (Parsecs)	Spectral Class	Apparent Magnitude (m)	Absolute Mag. (M)	Luminosity (Sun = 1)	Mass (Sun = 1)
1. Deneb	430	A2	1.26	−6.9	48,000	22*
2. Rigel A	250	B8	0.14	−6.8	43,500	21*
B	—	B9	6.6	−0.4	120	4*
3. Betelgeuse	150	M2	0.41	−5.5	13,000	red supergiant
4. Beta Crucis	150	B0	1.28	−4.6	5700	12*
5. Antares A	120	M1	0.92	−4.5	5200	red supergiant
B	—	B4	5.1	−0.3	110	4*
6. Beta Centauri A	90	B1	0.63	−4.1	3600	10*
B	—	?	4	−0.8	174	4*
7. Alpha Crucis A	120	B1	1.39	−4.0	3300	19*
B	—	B3	1.9	−3.5	2000	16*
8. Spica	80	B1	0.91	−3.6	2300	17*
9. Canopus	30	F0	−0.72	−3.1	1450	red giant
10. Achernar	20	B5	0.51	−1.0	200	4*
11. Capella A	14	G0	0.05	−0.7	150	red giant
B	—	M0	10.2	9.5	0.013	0.28*
C	—	M5	13.7	13	0.0005	red dwarf
12. Arcturus	11	K2	−0.06	−0.3	110	red giant
13. Aldebaran A	16	K5	0.86	−0.2	100	red giant
B	—	B3	13	12	0.0013	white dwarf
14. Vega	8	A0	0.04	0.5	52	3*
15. Pollux	12	K0	1.16	0.8	40	red giant
16. Sirius A	2.7	A1	−1.42	1.4	23	2.4
B	—	white dwarf	8.7	11.5	0.002	1.1
17. Fomalhaut A	7	A3	1.19	2.0	13	2*
B	—	K4	6.5	7.3	0.1	0.5*
18. Altair	5.1	A7	0.77	2.2	10	2*
19. Procyon A	3.5	F5	0.38	2.7	6.9	1
B	—	white dwarf	10.7	13	0.005	0.6
20. Alpha Centauri A	1.3	G2	−0.01	4.4	1.45	1.1
B	—	K5	1.4	5.8	1.25	0.9
C	—	M5	10.7	15	0.000083	?
SUN	0.000005	G2	−26.5	4.8	1.00	1.00

*Mass derived from mass-luminosity relationship.

Absolute magnitude (M) is the magnitude each star would show if it were exactly ten parsecs from earth. The sun's overwhelming apparent magnitude of m = —26.5 shrinks to an absolute magnitude of M = 4.8 under this system. Far from being the brighest star in the list, the sun is the dimmest except for some of the dwarf B and C components of multiple stars.

Luminosity refers to the actual amount of light energy that the star is putting out. In Table 11 luminosity is expressed by comparison to the sun's light output.

A chain of interlocking measurements goes into a listing such as Table 11. Luminosity is determined from absolute magnitude, which in turn is measured only after distances are found or estimated. And distance measurements depend, ultimately, on the value of the astronomical unit, which gives the length of our baseline. That is why astronomers are always eager to refine the measurement of the AU.

WEIGHING, WITH AND WITHOUT SCALES

Table 11 also lists the masses of the stars. As with distances, masses can be measured only for a small number of stars. For most stars, masses are inferred from indirect techniques.

Mass is measured by observing the gravitational pull one body exerts on another. The sun's mass was obtained by calculating its gravitational pull on earth. The stars are too far apart to exert any measurable gravitational effects on the solar system.

But some stars are binary or multiple systems. The stars of such systems are often as close to each other as the planets of the solar system are to the sun. Thus it is possible to observe the gravitational effects that these stars have on each other. In this manner, the masses of binary and multiple stars have been measured.

The technique has shortcomings. The stars being measured must be fairly close to each other. Sirius A and B are about 20 AU apart, for example; about the same separation as between the sun and the planet Uranus. Alpha Centauri A and B are close enough to each other to allow their masses to be measured, but Alpha Centauri C is more than 10,000 AU from its two companions, and its mass has not been determined.

Moreover, if a binary system is too far away from astronomers to measure the separation between the two stars, the masses cannot be measured. Single stars, of course, cannot be measured this way at all since there is no observable gravitational effect to work with.

Astronomers, however, have found another way to estimate the masses of some single stars. They long ago realized that the luminosity of a star is related to its mass. In 1924, Sir Arthur Eddington (1882–1944), the great English physicist, found that for main sequence stars, the luminosity varies as the 3.5 power of the mass. If you consider the sun as a starting point, with a mass and luminosity both set arbitrarily at 1, then Table 12 shows how luminosity changes with increasing mass.

TABLE 12: MASS-LUMINOSITY RELATIONSHIP

Mass		Luminosity
1	$1^{3.5} =$	1
5	$5^{3.5} =$	278
10	$10^{3.5} =$	3200
15	$15^{3.5} =$	13,100

As you can see, relatively small changes in mass bring about large differences in luminosity. Since the astronomer can measure luminosity and wants to derive mass, the luminosity is determined and its 3.5 root calculated.

Eddington also explained why this *mass-luminosity relationship* holds true. For stars that derive their energy from nuclear reactions and behave the way the sun does, the amount of matter in the star regulates the intensity with which the nuclear fusion can take place. Without going into further detail on the physics of the situation, we can simply state that the main sequence stars obey the mass-luminosity relationship well enough for us to be able to infer the masses of a great number of stars. But we must have some measure of a star's luminosity to get its mass. This, in turn, means we need a distance estimate. The shakier any one of these measurements is, the less reliable the final result.

GIANTS, DWARFS, AND MAIN SEQUENCE STARS

Table 11 shows a diversity among even its few stars that looks almost chaotic. Among thirty-three individual stars (eleven single stars, the rest in binary or multiple systems), we see every color of the spectrum, luminosities that range from 48,000 to 8.3×10^{-5} times the sun's, and masses that vary from nearly 20 to 0.29 solar masses. Stellar diameters also range from the supergigantic to the dwarfish.

Earlier in this chapter we said that there must be some governing physical principles behind the diversity of the stars. If there are, they are not obvious at first glance.

Before trying to uncover these governing principles, though, let's look a little more closely at the sizes of the stars. Very few stars are large enough and near enough to allow astronomers to measure their diameters directly.

For very big stars that are not too distant, the technique called *optical interferometry* is used. Two images of the star are focused into the telescope in such a way that their overlapping light waves will make a pattern that trained observers can translate into the star's diameter. To do this, a large crossbar is mounted atop the telescope, with mirrors on each end. Radio telescopes can also be turned into interferometers.

Since most stars are too far away or too small for the interferometry technique, their diameters are estimated in a subtler way: from a comparison of the star's surface temperature and total luminosity.

A star's surface temperature tells you how much energy each square centimeter of the surface is emitting. A hot, blue star with a surface temperature of 18,000°K, for example, is putting out three times the energy—per square centimeter —as the sun. The star's luminosity, though, depends on the energy emitted per square centimeter *and* the total surface area of the star; that is, the total number of square centimeters on the star's surface.

Thus, if you can determine the energy per square centimeter and the total luminosity, you can calculate the total surface area of the star. With that known, it is simple geometry to find the star's diameter.

While this method is indirect, its results agree with those from interferometry measurements when both techniques have been applied to the same star.

Considering only the stars of Table 11, stellar diameters range from more than 200 times the sun's, for supergiants such as Betelgeuse and Antares, to 0.0037 for Procyon B, the dwarf companion of the bright star Procyon. If Betelgeuse were where the sun is, it would swallow all the planets out to Mars. But the Pacific Ocean is wider than Procyon B.

By putting together the information we've gained so far on stellar luminosities, temperatures, masses, diameters, and so on, we can begin to see what the labels of Figure 7 really mean.

Blue Giants. These stars are highly luminous, massive, and hot, typically O or B spectral class. Rigel is a good example. Blue giants are also very young stars.

Rigel's age can be estimated in the following way. Rigel is 40,000 times more luminous than the sun. This means that it is converting its nuclear fuel to energy at a rate 40,000 times faster than the sun's. If the sun is losing four million tons of mass every second, Rigel is radiating away 160 billion tons of mass per second. From the mass-luminosity relationship, we can say that Rigel's mass is no more than 20 times the sun's. This means it has only 20 times the total fuel supply of our sun.

So Rigel is consuming its available nuclear fuel supply at a rate of $(40,000/20 = 2000)$ two thousand times the sun's consumption rate. If the sun is about five billion years old, then Rigel must be at least two thousand times younger, or it would have run out of fuel by now. Rigel is, then, no more than two and a half million years old. Among the stars, this is an infant.

Rigel is a new star, as are all the blue giants. New stars, then, must be in the process of creation all the time. Moreover, the blue giants must be quite short-lived; they exhaust their fuel supplies quickly.

The stars have always seemed eternal and unchanging to man. But although their lives are fantastically long compared to the life-span of a man, the stars do have life cycles of their own. They are born, age, and die. In fact, the human race is older than some blue giants.

If the blue giants are so short-lived, why are there so many of them on our list of the brightest stars? Simply because they are extremely luminous. A star such as Rigel, even at 250 parsecs' distance, outshines thousands of smaller and dimmer stars closer to earth.

Red Supergiants. These stars are apparently as massive as the blue giants, but they are much cooler. Their high luminosities are due to their enormous surface areas. Even though each square centimeter of surface is radiating weakly, there is so much surface area that the total luminosity is high. Two red supergiants, Betelgeuse and Antares, vary in brightness and are actually pulsating, "breathing" in and out in irregular patterns.

Astrophysicists believe the red supergiants to be young stars that are slowly contracting and growing hotter and that they may evolve into blue giant stars.

Main Sequence. This is the major family of stars. Main sequence stars tend to be stable, long-lived, and similar to the sun in most major features.

The place a star occupies along the main sequence line in an H-R diagram depends mainly on the star's mass. Mass has an important effect on both stellar luminosity and temperature. A star five times more massive than the sun would be some 278 times more luminous and would have a higher surface temperature. Its position in an H-R diagram would be higher up on the main sequence, more toward the upper left corner of the curve than the sun is.

A star's position on the main sequence curve, then, depends

largely on its mass. The more massive stars are higher up the line than the sun; the less massive stars are lower.

Red Dwarfs. Some stars, such as Alpha Centauri C, are so far down on the main sequence that they are called dwarfs (or, sometimes, subdwarfs). These stars are low in mass; hence their temperatures and luminosities are low. But their life-times can be extraordinarily long since they are consuming their nuclear fuel supplies slowly. Long after the sun has exhausted its hydrogen fuel, red dwarfs such as Alpha Centauri C will still be simmering along unchanged.

Red Giants. Stars such as Capella A, Arcturus, and Aldebaran A have surface temperatures that seem to be out of phase with their luminosities. Capella A, for example, has about the same temperature as the sun, but it is 150 times more luminous than the sun. Therefore, it must be larger than the sun, and is estimated to be about 16 times the sun's diameter.

For several reasons, astrophysicists consider the red giants to be older stars, which have used up much of their nuclear fuel and moved away from their original positions on the main sequence.

Since the red giants (and the red supergiants, too) do not obey the mass-luminosity relationship, their masses can only be guessed at unless they are members of binary or multiple systems and are close enough to earth for gravitational effects to be observed. This is evidence that the type of nuclear reactions that power the sun are not taking place in these types of stars.

White Dwarfs. About fifty years ago, the discovery of the white dwarf stars caused almost as much consternation in the astronomical world as today's uproar over the quasars.

Consider Sirius B and Procyon B, two classic white dwarfs.

Their A companions are both called Dog Stars because they are the brightest members of the constellations *Canis Major* and *Canis Minor*—the two dwarfs are called Pups. The Pups' masses have been measured quite satisfactorily; they are 1.1 and 0.6 solar masses, respectively. Their luminosities, though, are very low; therefore their diameters must be quite small. Sirius B is about twice earth's size, and Procyon B is almost as small as the moon. Yet their surface temperatures are very high, almost up to the levels of blue giants!

If the white dwarfs are that massive, that small, and that hot, then they are completely unlike any other type of star. For one thing, their densities must be fantastically high: a spoonful of white dwarf material would weigh tons on earth. But spectroscopic evidence shows that the white dwarfs are mainly hydrogen and helium, just as all the stars are.

The inescapable conclusion is that the white dwarfs are collapsed stars, stars in which the long tug-of-war between gravity and gas/radiation pressure has been won at last— by gravity.

Physicists have shown that it is possible to condense matter to the extremely high densities necessary to accept the col- lapsed-star idea. When these ultra-high-density conditions prevail, the matter is said to be in a *degenerate* state.

The white dwarfs give the appearance of stars that have exhausted their nuclear fuel and—with gas/radiation pres- sures gone—have collapsed under their own internal gravity. If so, they must be the most aged of stars.

Aged, but not necessarily old since massive stars go through their fuel supplies quickly. Something must happen to them, and perhaps the white dwarfs are the result. It is interesting to note that both Sirius A and Procyon A are rather hot, young stars. Perhaps their companions were once more mas-

The Orion Nebula, a vast cloud of gas and dust, lit by the energies of hot, young stars nearby (Mount Wilson and Palomar Observatories)

sive than they are now, ran through their fuel supplies quickly, exploded, and shrank to white dwarfdom. It is well established that stars explode.

EVOLUTIONARY TRACKS

The seeming chaos among the stars is starting to diminish and space is beginning to look a little more orderly. Stars are continually being born, living out certain life-spans, and then dying. The differences among the many types of stars are mainly differences in mass (and hence life expectancy) and age.

Astronomers say that stars *evolve*: change during their life-spans. The stars' lives are immensely longer than human history. The sun is about five billion years old, and a stellar infant such as Rigel is more than two million years old. Mankind as a species on earth is no older than Rigel. Civilization and astronomy both began merely ten thousand years ago. The first telescopes were built slightly more than 350 years ago; and radio astronomy is only 37 years old.

How can man hope to observe the full life-span of a star? It is impossible for any single star. But there are billions of stars to be seen, in every possible stage of stellar evolution. Even the handful plotted in the diagram at the beginning of this chapter shows, in a rudimentary way, the evolutionary stages of the stars. For that is what the H-R diagram really is: a plot of the evolutionary tracks of the stars.

Decades ago, theoretical work indicated that new stars are formed from the giant clouds of gas that can be seen in interstellar space. The accompanying photograph is of the Orion Nebula, a vast region thick with bright gas that reflects the light of hot, young stars nearby. Dark clouds, consisting of *interstellar dust,* cut across the luminous gas. The dust is grains of material, about 10^{-5} centimeters in size; microscopic, but a thousand times bigger than the individual atoms that comprise the interstellar gas.

The gas clouds are composed mainly of hydrogen and helium with a smattering of heavier elements, as are the stars themselves. The dust grains are of the same composition; apparently the grains are made up of gas atoms that have somehow linked together.

Von Weizsacker theorized that such clouds of gas and dust would develop turbulent eddies or whirlpools that will tend to suck additional matter into them. Soon—in astronomical time—these eddies can produce a body sizable enough to start attracting more material to itself through gravitational pull.

In time, this clump of gas and dust will grow to about a light year or more in diameter. The photograph on page 81 shows objects that fit this description very well. They are found in regions where gas, dust, and young stars predominate. The separate "little" clouds, each of them a light year or so across, are called *protostars:* that is, something that comes before a star is formed.

As the protostar grows, gravity begins to pull the cloud in on itself. As it collapses, the density at the center grows higher. As density increases, temperature rises. When the temperature reaches a certain point—probably around twenty million degrees—the hydrogen in the cloud starts to undergo nuclear fusion reactions and converts into helium. Tremendous energy is released. The dark protostar turns into a shining star.

All this theory is backed by observation. The two photographs on page 82 were taken at the Lick Observatory by George H. Herbig (born 1920). The first photo shows three

Part of the Rosette Nebula in the constellation Monoceros, a region of bright gas, dark dust, and young stars. Some of the smaller dark globules are presumed to be the beginnings of new stars; they are called protostars (Mount Wilson and Palomar Observatories)

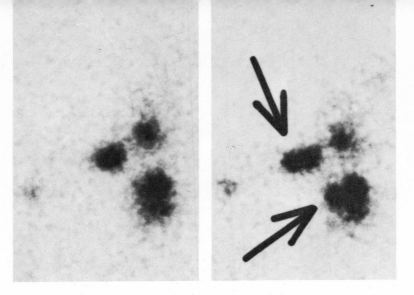

These negative prints show a region of the Orion Nebula where three faint, fuzzy stars were seen in 1947 (left), enmeshed in gas clouds. In 1954 (right) there were two additional stars that were not bright enough to be seen in the earlier photo. They may be new stars

stars, fuzzy in outline because they are still enmeshed in the gas cloud that surrounds them. The second picture, taken seven years later, shows the same spot in the sky. But two new stars are visible now. They were not shining in the first photo, presumably because they had not yet "turned on."

The gravitational collapse that turns a protostar into a true star can take place in a short time, by astronomical standards. For a star of the sun's mass, it could happen in something like one hundred million years; for stars of Rigel's mass, the collapse could be completed in one hundred thousand years.

Gravitational collapse occurs at the beginning of a star's life-span, when it is contracting from a protostar into a true star; and at the end, when it contracts into a white dwarf. Gravitational collapse has been suggested as one possible explanation for the energy source of the quasars. But whether the collapse is signifying the beginning of a quasar's life or the end of it has not yet been agreed upon.

Supergiant stars such as Betelgeuse may be in the last stages of contracting out of the protostar phase. Perhaps

Betelgeuse is shining by a combination of newly lit nuclear fire from its core and the energy of gravitation, which could cause some starshine of its own. Nineteenth-century physicists showed that gravitational energy could make the sun shine for a few million years, if the sun were slowly contracting. Probably gravitational energy can also light a protostar cloud during the final stages of contraction.

The H-R diagram shown in the beginning of this chapter is amended by Figure 10 to show the probable evolutionary track of the sun.

The star begins slightly to the right of the main sequence

Figure 10. A Hertzsprung-Russell diagram that shows the possible evolutionary track of the sun, which began as a collapsing cloud of gas and became a true star at point A some five billion years ago. In perhaps ten to fifteen billion years (point B), the sun will begin to change into a red giant star, then presumably will become a variable star and finally a white dwarf. The final stages of the sun's lifetime may be marked by nova explosions (after Struve)

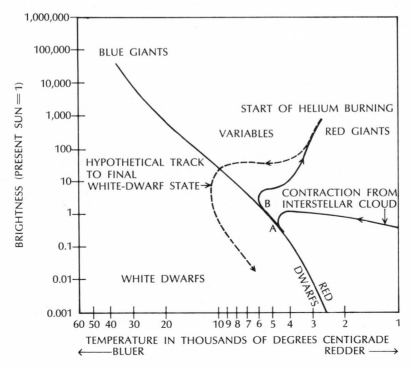

curve, as a protostar, and swings into the curve during its contraction phase. Its eventual place on the main sequence is determined mainly by its mass. When the star stops contracting and becomes stable, it resides on the main sequence for most of its lifetime. For the sun, this has already been about five billion years, and the best estimates are that the sun will remain a stable main sequence star for another ten billion years or so.

But eventually a star depletes its hydrogen fuel. Astrophysicists have shown that as the core of the star turns into helium, the central density begins to rise again. Thus the temperature at the core of the star rises as the helium content grows. This is contrary to what might be expected at first. Instead of cooling off as its fuel is used up, the star gets hotter. Much hotter.

When the helium content at the star's core is high enough, the density becomes so great that the central temperature rises to about 100 million degrees. At 20 million degrees, hydrogen fuses into helium. At 100 million degrees, helium begins to convert itself into carbon, oxygen, and neon.

The star has found a new energy source. But with a much higher central temperature, the outer layers of the star are pushed out farther than before. The star literally swells because the gas and radiation pressures that result from helium-fusion temperatures are higher than the pressures that were present when only hydrogen fusion was taking place. Gravity yields, and the star grows in size.

In terms of the evolutionary track on the H-R diagram, the star makes a right turn off the main sequence and enters the realm of the red giants. The surface temperature of the star is cooler than before because the surface layers are much farther from the center and have been thinned by their expansion. The star is more luminous, though, because it has gotten so big. In ten billion years or so, the sun will make this move, and eventually come to resemble a red giant such as Aldebaran.

The helium-fusion reactions go much faster than the earlier hydrogen fusion, and soon the helium supply of the star is dangerously low. Again, the core of the star has increased in density (because it is now made up of elements that are twelve to twenty times heavier than hydrogen). The temperature climbs again and reaches the point where oxygen, carbon, and neon start to fuse into still-heavier elements.

The cycle keeps repeating, but in ever-tightening coils: fusion reactions make heavier elements that increase the core density, which makes the core temperature rise, which leads to new fusion reactions that produce even heavier elements. Each new cycle goes faster than the one preceding it. The star is behaving like a Hemingway character who, when asked how he went bankrupt, replied: "Two ways . . . Gradually and then suddenly."

For the star is heading for disaster. New energy sources will not be forthcoming forever. Outwardly, the star continues to swell and its surface temperature gets lower. At some point, though, it turns back toward the left on the H-R diagram.

Just what happens next is not clear. It is known that there are pulsating stars in the region of the H-R diagram where the red giants are expected to make their "left turn" and head for extinction. The pulsating stars come in many different types; among the best known are the so-called *Cepheid* variables and *RR Lyrae* variables. Pulsating stars give the appearance of having reached a critical phase in their evolution. Gas and radiation pressures at the core may be starting to fail; gravity is beginning to pull the star back to a smaller size.

The pulsating stars are visible evidence of the battle between gas/radiation pressures and gravity. As the star swells, the outward-pushing pressures decrease; gravity gains the upper hand and the star begins to shrink. But in shrinking, the pressure forces build up again and the star is pushed outward again. For the Cepheid and RR Lyrae variables, these cycles are so regular that you can set your clock by them.

The pulsating stars can exist despite unbalanced pressure and gravitational forces because of a dynamic equilibrium: they pulsate, probably, because a stable configuration cannot be maintained any other way. The quasars' light and radio output varies dramatically over periods as short as a day or even less. Are the quasars pulsating?

Perhaps all stars go through a pulsating phase; perhaps not. In either case, the star eventually reaches a crisis. It has been producing constantly heavier elements in its core. Finally, the core consists largely of iron. Nuclear fusion reactions involving iron produce lighter elements, not heavier ones. The star has reached the end of its rope. It can produce no more energy in its core.

Rather suddenly, the gas/radiation pressures disappear. Gravity is still there, though, and the star collapses in on itself.

Possibly the star explodes. Many stellar explosions have been seen, some of them so catastrophic that they may completely demolish the star. Or the star may simply contract—with or without an explosion—down to the white dwarf stage.

Here the star has used up all its nuclear fuel supplies and collapsed down to a very small size. A slim rim of nuclear reactions may still be simmering near the star's surface; this would account for the high surface temperatures of the white dwarfs. But the core of the star is dead, degenerate matter, compressed to unbelievable density. Perhaps gravitational contraction energy is also helping to heat the white dwarfs. But they are slowly cooling off. Eventually the last erg of energy will be used up and the star will stop glowing altogether. It will then become a dark object, invisible to observation. Such is the probable fate of the sun.

In cases where the star goes through a catastrophic explosion, the only surviving remnant may be a weird, superdense neutron star. Only a few miles wide, yet almost as massive as the sun, the matter in a neutron star is packed so tightly that not even atomic nuclei can exist! Everything is crushed down into neutrons, which are so crowded that they cannot decay spontaneously into protons and electrons, as they do under more normal conditions.

In 1967, radio astronomers detected pulsed signals totally unlike any radio sources previously discovered. The pulses were as regular as clockwork—so precise, in fact, that some astronomers began speculating that they were being sent out by an intelligent civilization. It now appears, though, that the *pulsars* are neutron stars that are emitting natural radiowave energy. Radio astronomers located a pulsar in the heart of the Crab Nebula, the result of the stellar explosion in A.D. 1054, and early in 1969, this faint pulsar became the first to be seen visually and photographed.

This discussion of stellar evolutionary tracks has brought out a very important point. The stars are cosmic "cookers," manufacturing heavier elements out of hydrogen. Possibly, all the elements of the universe have been produced inside the stars. All except hydrogen.

The elements from helium to iron, we saw, are produced during a star's main sequence and red giant stages. The

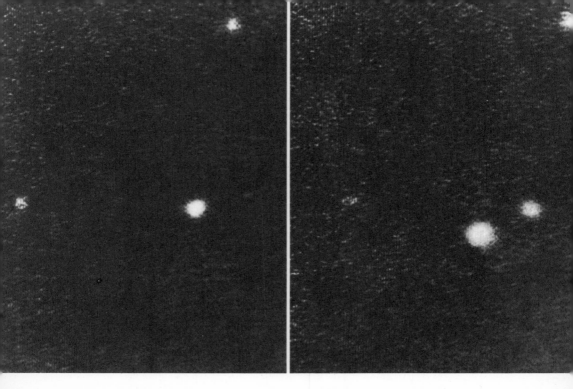

Photograph of the pulsar in the Crab Nebula. The picture at the left shows the pulsar "off"; only background stars are visible. The picture at the right shows the pulsar "on". This pulsar flashes on and off thirty-three times a second (Lick Observatory)

elements heavier than iron are presumably made during the brief but intense inferno of stellar explosions.

We can see a cycle now. Stars condense out of interstellar gas and dust and produce heavier elements inside themselves. During their lifetimes the stars eject some of their own material into space. Stars can spew material into space rather gently, as the sun does, or in violent explosions. In either event, this new material, containing heavier elements now, becomes part of the interstellar gas and dust from which new stars are built.

Thus we can see why some stars—such as the sun—contain a higher proportion of the heavier elements than other stars. The red giant stars, for example, are "metal poor," generally. This is because they were formed earlier than the sun and had less of the heavy material to draw on. The heavy elements they are producing internally are still inside them, in their cores, and will only gradually come to the surface— unless the star explodes, which brings most of the core material out into the open.

The sun is generally considered to be a "third generation" star. That is, the material from which the sun was built has been in two earlier generations of stars. This material was ejected from the stars, either peacefully or explosively, and became available to form the solar system. Your body, then, consists of atoms that were born inside an ancient star.

The earliest stars could have been made of nothing but hydrogen. The question is, where did this hydogen come from? Was it the original material of the universe? Was the universe nothing but hydrogen, in the beginning? The quasars play an important role in our thinking of cosmological matters.

STELLAR EXPLOSIONS

Stars explode. Solar flares are mild forms of explosion that happen many times each year on the sun. Although a solar flare is mild by stellar standards, it is an awesome event compared to the scale of human affairs.

A typical solar flare releases about 10^{33} ergs of energy. An erg is a small unit of energy: it represents the work done in moving a mass of one gram to an acceleration of one centimeter per second per second over a distance of one centimeter ($1 \text{ erg} = 1 \text{ gram} - cm^2/sec^2$). A fifty-watt lamp radiates half a billion ergs per second; it takes 10^{10} ergs per second to equal one kilowatt. But 10^{33} is a stupendous number. It would take the explosive force of more than 10^{10} megatons of TNT to equal 10^{33} ergs.

The sun radiates nearly 4×10^{33} ergs per second; therefore the energy that goes into a solar flare represents only about a quarter-second of the sun's total energy output. Solar flares are trivial compared to the total energy output of a star.

Incidentally, many other stars have been observed to show sudden increases of brightness, leading astronomers to suspect that they are also emitting flares. These so-called *flare stars* are mostly faint reddish dwarfs. Possibly larger and brighter stars give off flares too, but the flares are not bright enough to be seen against the background of the more luminous stars. Probably the sun's flares could not be detected from Alpha Centauri. Only when the star is inherently dim can flares be seen over interstellar distances.

Much more important than flares is the type of explosion called a *nova*. The word is from the Latin and means new. Back in pretelescope days, from time to time a new star would suddenly appear in the sky. After a few weeks or months it would fade back below the threshold of visibility. We know now that there was a star there all along, too faint to be seen. Its explosion made it bright enough to be observed as a nova star.

There are several different types of nova explosions, and almost as many theories as to what causes them. One thing seems certain: a nova star has reached a crucial point in its eternal battle of gravity versus pressure forces. In a nova explosion, the outward-pushing pressures win a temporary victory, and part of the star's material is blasted into space.

In a full-scale nova, a star of the sun's brightness will erupt into five thousand to one hundred thousand times its original luminosity. The peak of brightness is usually reached in a day or two; the star then settles back to its normal luminosity over the course of a few months.

Nova explosions seem to happen to stars that are more aged than the sun. Many nova stars are repeaters; they go through nova explosions as often as a dozen times a year, or as seldom as once a century. The fact that some nova stars repeat themselves shows that, despite the dramatic increase in brightness, the star has not been deeply damaged. At most the star blows off about a hundredth of its total mass. The outer layers of the star—corresponding, perhaps, to the chromosphere and upper photosphere—are blown into space. There they mix with the interstellar gases and add to the material available for building later-generation stars.

In terms of energy, a star of the sun's luminosity will use up about one thousand years' worth of energy output within a month during a nova explosion. Spectacular, but not much of a drain on a star that can remain luminous for billions of years.

Although a nova explosion does not seriously harm the star, our planet would very likely be wiped clean of all life if the sun went into a nova phase. The sun would eject a shell of gas that would be at least several thousand degrees hot. Our atmosphere could be boiled away; if the oceans were not vaporized in the first flash of heat, they would soon be evaporated, without the air to protect them from the sun's direct rays. Flammable things like forests, cities, and people would probably be ignited.

A *supernova* explosion is the ultimate in stellar violence. The Crab Nebula was the supernova that exploded on A.D. July 4, 1054. Oriental astronomers noted the "new" star in their records, when it was bright enough to be seen in full daylight—without a telescope. Those wildly distorted gases are still moving outward from the original explosion at speeds of several hundred kilometers per second.

In a supernova, the star releases all the energy it has, as much as 10^{51} ergs—more than a billion years worth of energy —in one titanic blast. The explosion is so shattering that most—possibly all—of the star's substance is hurled outward at speeds of 1000 km/sec. The star flames to a radiance one hundred million times brighter than the sun. There may be a faint dwarf star left after the explosion, or the star may be entirely destroyed. If the sun went into a supernova explosion, the whole solid body of the earth might be vaporized, and the sun itself would either be totally destroyed or become a white dwarf.

Not every star will become a supernova. In fact, supernova explosions are comparatively rare. The last supernova in our own Milky Way galaxy occurred in 1572, about forty years too early for the telescope. It has been estimated that supernovas happen in our galaxy once every three hundred to five hundred years. Supernovas are so brilliant, however, that they can be seen in other galaxies, millions of parsecs away. All the modern studies of supernovas are of explosions that have taken place in neighboring galaxies.

Even though they are rare events, supernovas probably account for a good deal of the heavy elements in the Milky Way and, presumably, in other galaxies. Calculations have shown that even if supernovas occur only once every five hundred years, their output of elements heavier than iron is still enough to account for the observed abundances of these elements.

There is even observational evidence that heavier-than-iron elements are formed in supernova explosions. The heaviest element found naturally on earth is uranium (atomic weight

238). Uranium and several of the other heavy elements are radioactive; they decay spontaneously into lighter elements and eventually end as lead, helium, and so on. In nuclear physics laboratories, scientists have produced even heavier elements. But they decay quickly, sometimes in minutes.

There is no reason to assume that elements heavier than uranium have not been produced naturally on earth. But in the five-billion-year history of this planet, these short-lived elements disappeared long ago, transmuted into lighter elements. Eventually the same thing will happen to uranium and all the other radioactives.

Many supernovas show a sharp peak of light output that dims rapidly in about fifty-five days and then continues to dim on a slower basis for months or even years afterward. That fifty-five-day peak, though, reminds physicists of the behavior of the man-made radioactive element, Californium (atomic weight 252). Californium has a fifty-five-day "half life"; that is, in fifty-five days, half of a given amount of the element will have decayed into lighter elements.

Do these supernovas shine with the energy of heavy-element reactions? The evidence seems to point that way. Spectra of some red giant stars have even shown the presence of Technetium (atomic weight 99), a man-made element on earth. Technetium in these stars can hardly be more than a few hundred thousand years old. It was produced in the red giants, and recently.

Supernova remnants are strong radio sources. Even when there is little to be seen optically, as in Cassiopeia A, the radio energy is there. The Crab Nebula (Taurus A to radio astronomers) is another powerful radio source, the strongest in our galaxy.

The type of radio emission given off by supernova remnants such as the Crab Nebula was something of a puzzle to astronomers. It was not the kind of radio emission that could be coming from a simple hot gas or plasma. In the 1950's, I. S. Shklovsky (born 1916) of the Soviet Union suggested that this radio output is due to *synchrotron* radiation.

The synchrotron is a type of particle accelerator used by nuclear physicists to probe the behavior of subatomic particles. Here again, nuclear physics has paid off handsomely for astrophysics. For in synchrotrons, when electrons are accelerated by powerful magnetic fields until they reach velocities close to the speed of light, they give off a type of radiation that is very similar to the radio emissions received from the Crab Nebula. The Crab Nebula, then, is a sort of gigantic natural synchrotron, where strong magnetic fields are causing electrons to whirl around at near-light speeds and emit radiation. The radio sources outside our galaxy—including the quasars—are all of the synchrotron type.

The synchrotron theory was subjected to a simple test. If the radio emission from the Crab Nebula were caused by synchrotron processes, then much of the Nebula's light emission would be due to the same cause. If so, the light would be polarized—that is, the light waves should be lined up more or less in a single plane, for any given wavelength, rather than arranged randomly. As the accompanying photographs show, the light from the Crab Nebula is indeed heavily polarized. The synchrotron theory is most likely correct; we know what causes the radio and light emission from the Nebula.

But none of the energy processes that power stars during their main sequence and red giant phases can provide an explanation for the titanic energy output of the quasars—if

Polarized light from the Crab Nebula. When polarizing filters are placed on the telescope, the Crab Nebula shows different appearances. If the light were unpolarized, the Nebula would look the same in each photograph. Polarized light is evidence that the Crab Nebula's light comes from synchrotron radiation (Mount Wilson and Palomar Observatories)

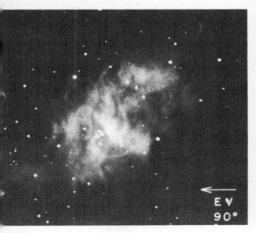

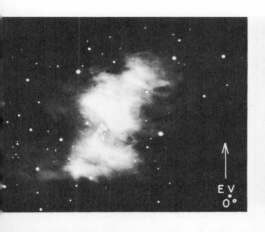

the quasars are indeed the most distant objects yet observed. The quasars may be putting out so much energy that even nuclear fusion is simply too weak to do the job!

But the energy released in a supernova explosion is immensely greater than ordinary fusion reactions provide. A single supernova explosion could not explain the quasars, any more than a single spark in a cylinder of your car will keep the engine running all day. But if there could somehow be a chain of supernova explosions. . . .

5

Galaxies

It often happens in astronomy
that conservative ideas
do not pay very well,
especially when dealing
with a quite new phenomenon.

Fred Hoyle

THE UNIVERSE IS POPULATED BY GALAXIES, JUST AS A CITY IS populated by people. People are made up of individual cells, and galaxies are composed of individual stars. Galaxies are apparently the largest units into which stars are incorporated; there are smaller groupings of stars, such as clusters and associations, but no larger star formation has been found. The quasars may be as large as some galaxies. In fact, some astronomers feel that quasars *are* galaxies of an unusual sort.

One of the large types of standard galaxies, with a star population of roughly one hundred billion, is the Milky Way. To date, more than a billion other galaxies have been observed. The deeper man peers into space, the more and more galaxies he sees: giant islands of stars set in the vast sea of space.

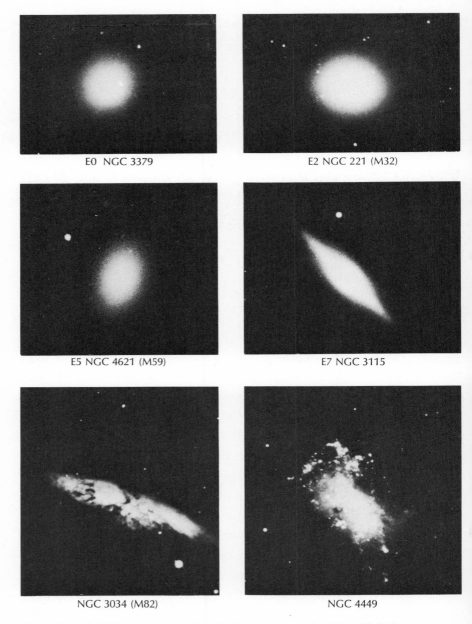

E0 NGC 3379

E2 NGC 221 (M32)

E5 NGC 4621 (M59)

E7 NGC 3115

NGC 3034 (M82)

NGC 4449

Examples of different types of galaxies as categorized by Hubble. Elliptical galaxies start with E0, which are most nearly spherical, and go to E7, which are considerably flattened. Spirals are rated a, b, or c, depending on the tightness of their spiral-arm windings. Barred

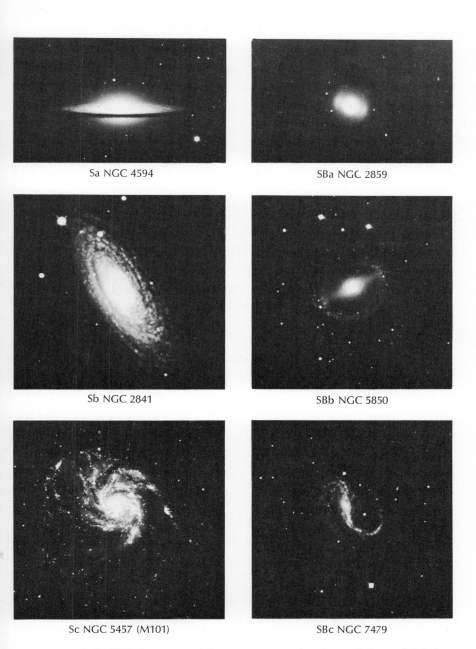

Sa NGC 4594

SBa NGC 2859

Sb NGC 2841

SBb NGC 5850

Sc NGC 5457 (M101)

SBc NGC 7479

spirals (SB) have a straight segment coming from their nuclei before the spiral arms begin. Irregular galaxies such as NGC 3034 and NGC 4449 do not fit into either the elliptical or spiral pattern (Mount Wilson and Palomar Observatories)

Galaxies range from immense globular shapes that dwarf the Milky Way to relatively tiny, amorphous smudges that are almost too small to be dignified with the name galaxy. Some galaxies are pouring out enormous amounts of radio energy, while some appear to be in the process of exploding. The Milky Way, recent evidence shows, may well have exploded not too long ago as astronomers reckon time.

Galaxies can be grouped into general classes so that different types may be identified. Edwin P. Hubble (1889–1953), a pioneer investigator of galaxies outside the Milky Way, put together such a classification more than forty years ago. The photographs on pages 98–99 show the major types of galaxies, according to Hubble's classification scheme.

THE MILKY WAY

Until the 1920's, most astronomers felt that the Milky Way was the entire universe and that everything that could be seen in the sky was inside it. There were others, though, who thought that the Milky Way was only one star-island among many.

But neither side had enough evidence to prove its point. No one could measure the distance to anything more than a few parsecs away. No one knew the shape or extent of the Milky Way. Not even the position of the sun within the Milky Way was known.

Most astronomers believed that the sun was near the center of the Milky Way and could point to strong evidence to support this. A few, most notably Harlow Shapley (born 1885), argued that the sun was far off to one side of the Milky Way, tens of thousands of light years from its center.

Consider their problem. You are chained to a cloudy planet and asked to determine the shape and extent of the star system in which you are embedded. It is like being locked in one room of a vast building all your life and trying to figure out how the building looks from the outside. To make matters worse, the only window in the room is frosted!

Many astronomers, since the time of Sir William Herschel (1738–1822), had tackled the problem of the Milky Way's size and shape. For more than a century they had all come up with the same answer—and it was wrong.

How would you handle the problem? If you can see the Milky Way tonight, try thinking about it. A narrow band of light arches across the sky. With a good telescope, you can see that this band is made up of stars. With more powerful telescopes, millions upon millions of stars become visible. How can you determine the size and shape of the Milky Way? One obvious way is to count the stars in every direction and see where they are thickest and where they thin out. This is a hopeless task since there are so many stars.

To get around this difficulty, astronomers selected certain small areas, all of the same angular size, carefully spotted in all quarters of the sky, and counted stars in those areas. They quickly found that the Milky Way is a rather flat disc of stars, as you would suspect from looking at it with the naked eye. Our solar system is close to the central plane of this disc. But how far does the disc extend? Is it farther in some directions than in others? Star counts by the best of half a dozen generations of astronomers showed conclusively that the star-disc extended for just about the same distances in every direction. The conclusion was that the sun is very nearly at the center of the Milky Way.

The idea that the sun is at the center of the galaxy—

A globular star cluster in the constellation Hercules. The stars in the center of this cluster are probably packed as closely as the planets of our solar system (Mount Wilson and Palomar Observatories)

perhaps at the center of the entire universe!—profoundly disturbed many astronomers and philosophers. If Copernicus had taught mankind one thing, it was that man should not expect to be at the center of creation. But the evidence showed that we were!

To find the evidence that would dispute this conclusion, Shapley studied the seemingly symmetrical arrangement of stars around the sun. There are about 100 objects in the sky called *globular clusters*. To the naked eye they appear as rather fuzzy fourth-magnitude stars. But as the accompanying photograph shows, in the telescope they can be seen to be mammoth clusters of stars. Globular clusters range from 20 to 100 parsecs in diameter and contain from 100,000 to a million stars. The brightest stars are red giants; there are no young blue giants present, and very little—if any—interstellar gas and dust. Pulsating stars of the RR Lyrae and Cepheid variable types are plentiful in these clusters.

This led to two conclusions: (1) the globular clusters are very old, older than the stars close to the sun; and (2) because they are so faint, even though huge, they must be much more distant from the sun than most of the stars visible from earth.

But what most interested Shapley was that the globular clusters were all concentrated in one region of the sky instead of being spread symmetrically all around the heavens. One-third of all the globular clusters known can be found in a 2 percent area of the sky, in the region of the constellation Sagittarius.

The globular clusters may actually be grouped on one side of the Milky Way, Shapley reasoned. Or they may be spread symmetrically around the center of the Milky Way, and we see them concentrated in one area because we on earth are actually far off to one side of the Milky Way.

The second alternative seemed much more reasonable and elegant to Shapley—but he had to prove its validity.

An important part of the proof would be measurements of the distances of the globular clusters from the sun.

MILEPOSTS IN THE SKY

The globular clusters were much too far away to use parallax measurements. But the pulsating stars in the clusters have turned out to be mileposts allowing astronomers to measure the distances not only to the globular clusters, but even to other galaxies.

For many years, stars such as the Cepheid variables and RR Lyrae variables were known to pulsate in precise, regular patterns. The Cepheids are named after Delta Cephei, the fourth-brightest star in the constellation Cepheus. Because it was the first of its type to be studied carefully, it has lent its name to all the Cepheids. RR Lyrae is in the constellation Lyra, and was also the first of its type to be studied well; its name is used for all the variables of the same type.

Unlike irregular variables like Betelgeuse (and the quasars), the Cepheids and RR Lyrae variables pulsate so exactly that astronomers have jokingly made as if they set their watches by them. Cepheids, among the most luminous of stars, are typically several thousand times more luminous than the sun. Their pulsations range from periods of one to one hundred days. RR Lyrae variables are typically some one hundred times brighter than the sun, and their periods go from about seven to sixteen hours.

Each star of these types has its own period of pulsation

from which it does not vary. For example, Polaris, the north star, is a Cepheid variable with a period of just under four days: every 3 days, 23 hours, 13 minutes, and 31 seconds, Polaris goes from its dimmest magnitude (m = 2.6) to its brightest (m = 2.5). The difference in magnitude is too small to measure with anything less than sensitive professional equipment; but the timing is breathtakingly consistent. And it is that way for all the Cepheids and RR Lyrae variables.

To a romanticist, these stars might almost seem to be deliberately calling attention to themselves. In 1910, Henrietta Leavitt (1868–1921), a researcher at the Harvard Observatory, paid heed to that call.

Miss Leavitt was studying photographs of the stars in the Magellanic Clouds, the two dwarf galaxies that appear to be satellites of the Milky Way. She noted that the longer the period of pulsation of the Cepheids in the Clouds, the brighter the stars' apparent magnitudes. She concluded that all Cepheids, everywhere, were of the same nature: the longer the period, the brighter the star.

Shapley and others leaped on this clue. They made a bold assumption: since the Magellanic Clouds are so small in comparison to their distance from earth, the individual differences in distance among the Cepheids in the Clouds could be ignored. Practically speaking, they reasoned, all the Cepheids in the Clouds are at the same distance from us. This is like saying that all the people in Sicily are at the same distance from Philadelphia; it is not precisely true, but the differences in distance from one person to another in either place are small enough to ignore, compared to the distance between the two regions.

If all the Cepheids in the Clouds are assumed to be at roughly the same distance from earth, then their apparent magnitudes can be equated to their absolute magnitudes and luminosities. Distance is the difference between apparent and absolute magnitudes.

Therefore, the period of a Cepheid is directly linked not only to its apparent magnitude, but to its absolute magnitude and luminosity as well. By timing a Cepheid's period of pulsation, you can tell its luminosity, no matter where it is in the sky. It works this way: Cepheids with periods of 100 days have been observed to be three magnitudes brighter than 10-day Cepheids. From our knowledge of the relationship of magnitude to luminosity we can say that the 100-day Cepheids are 2.512^3, about 16 times more luminous than 10-day Cepheids.

Armed with this knowledge, Shapley realized that if the distance to a single Cepheid, anywhere, could be measured and its true luminosity thereby fixed in terms of the sun's luminosity, then the true luminosities of all the Cepheids everywhere could be learned merely by timing their pulsations. And once true luminosity is known, the distance to each star can be easily determined by comparing its apparent magnitude to its absolute magnitude.

This is the reverse of the way things are normally done, of course. For stars close enough to the sun, you measure the distance and then compare the apparent magnitude with the distance to get absolute magnitude and luminosity. But for the Cepheids, the pulsations make it possible to learn luminosity and then distance. The inverse-square rule is used in reverse, but it is still the heart of the distance measurement.

Shapley was able to estimate the distances of the globular clusters from earth by timing some of the variables in them. From this, he inferred the distance to the center of the galaxy. He overestimated this distance, for reasons we will see shortly, but he was right in his hypothesis that the globular clusters form a roughly spherical "halo" around the center of the galaxy, and the solar system is far removed from the center of the Milky Way.

There is a chance that the quasars resemble the globular clusters in several aspects. Some astronomers feel that the quasars may be massive objects, about the size and mass of globular clusters, and may also be arranged in something like a "halo" around our galaxy.

THE MILKY WAY'S STRUCTURE

Shapley was basically right about the position of the sun in the Milky Way. We know today that the sun is about 10,000 parsecs from the center of the Milky Way. But Shapley also firmly believed that the Milky Way encompassed all the observable universe, including the many so-called "spiral nebulae" that we know now to be separate galaxies.

In a famous debate in Washington before the National Academy of Science on April 26, 1920, Shapley argued his case against Heber D. Curtis of the Lick Observatory. Curtis (1872–1942) held that the sun was near the center of the Milky Way, and the "spiral nebulae" were outside the Milky Way.

Both men were right and wrong, though the argument was not really settled for several more years. In 1924, Hubble announced that he had observed Cepheid variables in a few of the spiral nebulae. The Cepheids showed apparent magnitudes of about m = 18. Their distances, therefore, were calculated to be at least half a million light years. This distance was far greater than anyone had suspected previously. It satisfied most astronomers that the "nebulae" were actually galaxies in their own right, separate from the Milky Way.

Gradually, astronomers came to realize why the earlier star-counting technique had given them a completely wrong picture of the Milky Way. They found that their vision had been obscured by a smokescreen—clouds of interstellar dust had prevented them from seeing the heavens as they really are. As Figure 11 shows, clouds of dust lie along the plane of the Milky Way, in the neighborhood of the sun.

When astronomers from Herschel on down had tried to count stars in all directions, the dust formed a veil that increasingly obscured the light of the stars at greater and greater distances. The astronomers were like men trying to count street lamps in a heavy fog. They could see only a few.

Figure 11. A cross-section of the Milky Way galaxy

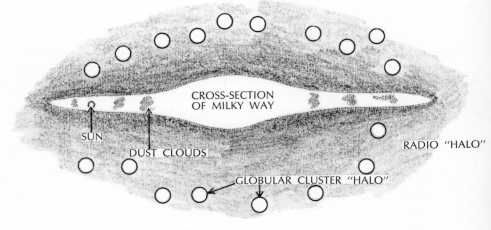

The farther lamps were dimmed by the fog, and those still farther away were completely blanketed and invisible.

Shapley could see the globular clusters at great distances because they are high above and far below the dust-strewn central plane of the galaxy. But the dust dimmed even the clusters enough to confuse Shapley's distance measurements and to cause him to overestimate the distance of the sun from the center of the Milky Way by more than 50 percent. Hubble and others could study the outside galaxies because they, too, can be seen above and below the dust lanes. In fact, Hubble was at first puzzled by the "zone of avoidance" around the Milky Way's central plane, where no outside galaxies could be found. That in itself was an important clue that something was clouding visibility along the galactic plane.

In addition, once astronomers started paying attention to the outside galaxies (thanks largely to the 100-inch Mt. Wilson telescope, which went into action in 1918), they saw that many of the spiral galaxies were flattened discs with heavy lanes of dust along their spiral arms. In other words, some of the spiral galaxies began to look as though they might be similar in structure to the Milky Way.

The photograph on page 111 shows M 31, the beautiful spiral in Andromeda, which is now thought to be a fairly good model of what the Milky Way looks like. At a distance of some two million light years, M 31 is the closest large spiral to the Milky Way; but other, smaller galaxies are closer.

The central regions of M 31 are much more thickly massed with stars than are the spiral arms; this is true of the spiral galaxies in general. In the Milky Way, our solar system is in one of the spiral arms, and the star-rich core of our galaxy is forever hidden from our sight by the interstellar dust that swirls through the arms. If there were no dust, our night sky would blaze with the brightness of billions of stars, a brightness that would rival daylight.

But the dust is there, and the galaxy's heart is hidden by it. When the full impact of this "dust curtain" hit astronomers, in the late 1920's, they became very gloomy about learning much about the Milky Way's structure.

Optical mapping of the Milky Way consists of tracing the positions of luminous O and B-class blue giant stars and bright clouds of hydrogen such as the Orion Nebula. Much less is seen, because of the "dust curtain," but it is seen with greater detail. This technique can be carried out to a distance of about 6000 parsecs before the interstellar dust shuts off any further observations.

In 1931, however, Karl Jansky (1905–50) inadvertently opened up the new field of radio astronomy. World War II put a temporary halt to this promising field, but by the early 1950's radio astronomers were busily mapping out the spiral structure of the galaxy. They tuned in on the 21-cm wavelength emitted by the clouds of hydrogen in the Milky Way's spiral arms. The 21-cm "song of hydrogen" penetrates the interstellar dust easily. The 21-cm map of the Milky Way in Chapter 1 traces the hydrogen gas clouds that thread their way through the galaxy's arms and even penetrate to the core.

By combining optical and radio measurements, the size and shape of the Milky Way have been determined to a reasonably good accuracy. Our galaxy is approximately 100,000 light years in diameter, with the sun located in a spiral arm about 30,000 light years (or 10,000 parsecs) from the center. The core of the Milky Way bulges to a thickness of some 20,000 light years, while the spiral arms are much thinner. It looks almost as though our Milky Way—and

The beautiful spiral galaxy M 31 in the constellation Andromeda is probably similar in appearance to the Milky Way (Mount Wilson and Palomar Observatories)

most spiral galaxies—consisted of two subsystems: a spheroidal core, and thin, flat spiral arms.

The types of stars found in the two sections differ markedly. In the spiral arms are the young blue giants and the clouds of gas and dust from which they are formed; the sun is a rather old star for this region of the galaxy. In the central spheroid, or core, are mostly older stars; red giants are the brightest types. There are no bright gas nebulas or dark formations of dust (at least, none have been found in the cores of other spiral galaxies).

Walter Baade (1893–1960) of Mt. Palomar started the convention of calling the stars near the sun *Population I* and the older, core stars *Population II*. This can cause some confusion, especially since the Population II stars are thought to be "first generation" and the Population I stars are "second generation" or later. By first generation, we mean the oldest stars, stars that probably formed directly from the original gas clouds. Second and later generation stars formed after the interstellar gases had been enriched with heavy elements, thanks to the ejection of matter by first generation stars during their main sequence, red giant, and explosion phases.

First generation or Population II stars are very low in metal content. This is to be expected, if they formed from gas clouds that contained only hydrogen or, at most, hydrogen and helium. There are no blue giants among Population II; these short-lived types passed into white dwarfdom or extinction eons ago, spreading their heavy-element content back into space as they died away. The younger, Population I stars have significant heavy-element contents since they were formed out of clouds that already contained heavy elements.

And, of course, there are young blue giants in Population I.

The same situation is seen in other spiral galaxies. The central regions contain Population II stars; the spiral arms have predominantly Population I stars.

The evidence gained from studying the H-R diagrams of the globular clusters that "halo" the Milky Way suggests that they are probably the oldest stars of the Milky Way: red, low in heavy elements, and pulsating stars predominate in the globular clusters. Other galaxies, both spiral and elliptical, are also surrounded by globular cluster halos. Individual globular clusters have even been seen at distances of about 80,000 parsecs, which means that they may be independent of our galaxy altogether, existing on their own. Were they somehow "shot" out of the Milky Way? One possible explanation for the quasars is that they are massive objects ejected from our own or some other galaxy (or galaxies). Do the "independent" globular clusters lend weight to this idea?

Radio studies have shown that the Milky Way (and other galaxies as well) is surrounded by a faint "radio halo"; that is, 21-cm radiation is apparently being generated from the region all around the galaxy. This means that there must be hydrogen gas there, although it is too thin to be seen optically. Some astronomers think that this radio halo is due to gas that has been blown outward from the central regions of the Milky Way.

Incidentally, the most recent radio findings show that about 1 percent of the mass of the Milky Way is interstellar gas, mainly hydrogen. This figure is much lower than previous estimates. It is from this 1 percent that new stars are being manufactured, and the ejection of matter by aging stars contributes to this interstellar "building fund."

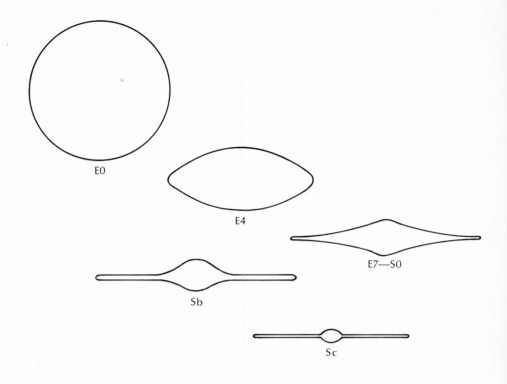

EO

E4

E7—S0

Sb

Sc

VARIOUS IRREGULAR AND DWARF SYSTEMS

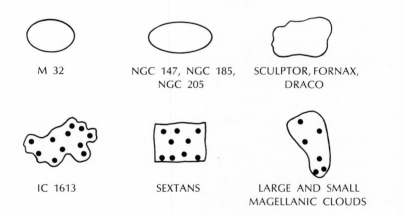

M 32

NGC 147, NGC 185,
NGC 205

SCULPTOR, FORNAX,
DRACO

IC 1613

SEXTANS

LARGE AND SMALL
MAGELLANIC CLOUDS

Figure 12. One suggested classification of galaxies is based on two characteristics: the mass and degree of flattening as charted in the diagram (after Arp)

GALAXIES BY THE GROUP

There are three major types of galaxies: elliptical, spiral, and irregular. The ellipticals are numbered, in Hubble's system, from E0 to E7, depending on their flatness and rotation rate. E0 galaxies are actually spherical and are the largest galaxies of all, as Figure 12 shows. The spirals are given letters a, b, or c, according to the tightness of their windings.

Why do one hundred billion or so stars form a spiral arrangement in one case and an elliptical one in another? This is a central problem in astronomy and cosmology, a problem that has received no convincing answer thus far.

Many cosmologists have tried to find some pattern to the various types of galaxies, some scheme that will show how a galaxy might evolve from one sort to another. At present, most students in this field believe that galaxies do not evolve one from another: spirals stay spiral, ellipticals remain elliptical, and irregulars are always that way. In fact, no one has come up with a satisfactory theory about how galaxies come into being.

While galaxies are the largest collections of stars, galaxies themselves form into larger groupings, usually called clusters.

The Milky Way, M 31, and fifteen smaller galaxies make up a system that is bound together by gravitational forces. This bears the prosaic name of the *Local Group*. The Milky Way and M 31, practically twins, are on opposite sides of the Group—about two million light years apart—with the smaller galaxies scattered between them for the most part. There are three spirals (M 33 being the other one), ten ellipticals and four irregular galaxies.

The Local Group is a small and rather poor cluster of galaxies. There are clusters that contain thousands of galaxies. In fact, it now appears that all of the billions of galaxies that have been observed are arranged into various clusters. The clusters themselves may be grouped into still larger systems, which have been dubbed *superclusters*.

The largest clusters of galaxies seem to contain mainly elliptical members. Fred Hoyle of Cambridge University points out that these clusters are almost always centered on a massive E0 galaxy—typically ten to one hundred times more massive than the Milky Way and up to ten times more luminous.

RADIO GALAXIES

The Milky Way has been mapped by radio telescopes and has a faint radio halo surrounding it. The same holds true for M 31 and most other galaxies. Within the Milky Way there are discrete radio sources, such as the Crab Nebula, which have been found to be remnants of ancient supernova explosions.

Discrete radio sources are also found outside the Milky Way. More than 3000 discrete radio sources have been located by radio telescopes so far, and radio astronomers expect to find 100,000 or more when detailed radio surveys of the entire sky are completed. Hundreds of these radio sources have been identified optically as galaxies. Most have not been identified at all. More than 200 of the sources are known to be quasars.

Most galaxies are much like the Milky Way in radio emission, radiating about 10^{38} ergs/sec of radio energy. This is equal to 10^{28} kilowatts. Since a large spiral galaxy pours out about 10^{44} ergs/sec in visible light, the radio output is only a millionth of the optical power. Clearly the Milky Way—and most galaxies—are not especially energetic in radio output. Radio astronomers call them "normal" galaxies, and reserve the title, "radio galaxies" for the galaxies that perform more spectacularly.

Many radio galaxies put out a hundred times the radio energy that the Milky Way does; others are a thousand and even a million times more energetic in radio emission than normal galaxies. The quasars, if they are distant objects, have at least a million times the Milky Way's radio power. The quasars, of course, appear very bright visually. But the radio galaxies do not seem to be unusually bright in optical wavelengths, at least, not at first glance.

There are two major types of radio galaxies. The first type is "bright" (to radio telescopes) mainly in the galaxy's core. They may be either spiral or elliptical galaxies. The radio intensity of these "core-emission" radio galaxies may range from one hundred to several thousand times that of normal galaxies.

The great elliptical galaxy, M 87, is a startling case. M 87 is one of the largest and (optically) brightest galaxies known; it is the most important member of the Virgo cluster of galaxies. To the radio astronomers, M 87 is known as Virgo A. The photograph at the top of page 119 shows a long-exposure photograph of M 87; the central, star-thick, core of the galaxy was overexposed so that the fainter outer stars and surrounding halo of globular clusters could register on the film.

When radio astronomers found unusually strong signals

coming from the core of Virgo A, optical astronomers tried taking short-exposure photographs of the region to see if there was some detail that the long-exposure photos had washed out. They found a jet of glowing plasma streaking off to one side of the core!

Nothing like this had ever been seen before. At the core of M 87 is a small, intensely bright central spot, with the 10,000-parsec-long jet coming out of it (see the smaller photograph). Both the central spot and the jet are bluish in color, and the light is highly polarized, just as the light of the Crab Nebula is polarized. This means that the radio emission and the light are caused by synchrotron radiation.

M 87's jet must be at least thirty thousand years old since it could not have reached its present size in less than that time unless it traveled faster than light. The gases in the jet are probably moving at high speeds, perhaps close to the speed of light, although accurate measurement of their velocity has not been possible. So the best we can say is that the jet is more than thirty thousand years old and probably much less than a million years old.

It certainly looks as though something violent happened in M 87's core—yesterday, on the galactic time scale.

The second type of radio galaxy has two radio-bright regions, and instead of being associated with the core of the galaxy, these regions are off on either side of the galaxy; to the eye, out in seemingly empty space. These "double" sources may or may not have strong radio emission at their cores as well. Many quasars are known to be double sources, although in the case of 3C 273, the brightest and most-studied quasar, there are two visible components giving off the radio energy.

The elliptical galaxy M 87 in a long-exposure photograph (below) and a short-exposure photograph (right), showing its bright core and "jet" (Mount Wilson and Palomar Observatories)

The strongest radio galaxy known is Cygnus A, which emits on the order of a million times the radio output of the Milky Way. Cygnus A has two radio-emission regions in its core and two large powerful regions outside its visible body, about one hundred thousand light years on either side of the galaxy (see the sketches at right).

A few years ago, many astronomers felt that Cygnus A and similar sources were two galaxies in the process of colliding. They look unusual enough to lead to that conclusion. But calculations showed that even a galactic collision could not provide enough energy to account for the powerful radio emission. And the way the radio source is split leads to the impression that something exploded at the core of the galaxy and hurled radio-bright material outward and away from the core.

The double radio sources are attributed to synchrotron radiation. This is also called *nonthermal* radiation.

Radiation from the sun or a star is due to thermal processes. Heat makes the plasma glow with light; also, but invisible to our eyes, the plasma "glows" in infrared and radio wavelengths. If the plasma is hot enough, it may also emit considerable ultraviolet, x-ray, and even gamma-ray radiation. Thermal sources can be easily identified by the fact that the energy coming from them is strongest at the shorter wavelengths. The sun, for example, emits much more energy in visible wavelengths than it does in the radio regions of the spectrum.

The radio galaxies, however, show just the opposite characteristic. Their radio emission increases in intensity as the wavelength gets longer, a type of radiation also observed in synchrotrons, where electrons are accelerated to nearly the speed of light by powerful magnetic fields. The Crab Nebula

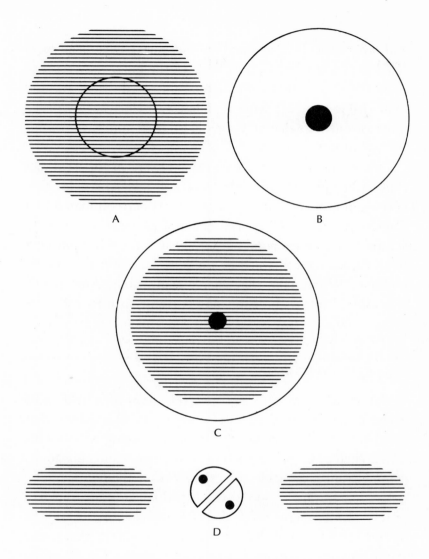

Figure 13. Types of radio galaxies. Drawing A shows a normal galaxy, such as the Milky Way, as seen from above its north pole. The shaded region shows the area of radio emission. B is a "core emission" type of radio galaxy. C shows the radio emission areas of M 87, a strong source at the core and an extended region slightly smaller than the visible galaxy. D is a "double" source, such as Cygnus A. Some double sources also have radio activity in their cores, which may also be split into two regions (after Heeschen)

and other supernova remnants in our galaxy have been identified as synchrotron sources. So have the radio galaxies; they show the same type of nonthermal energy distribution, and their visible light is polarized. These two clues have satisfied most astronomers that all the radio galaxies (and the quasars) are synchrotron sources.

This means that the radio-emission regions of these galaxies contain hot plasmas with electrons and magnetic fields that have enormous amounts of energy. It has been estimated that Cygnus A has a total energy bankroll of some 10^{60} ergs to account for its huge radio output. That is roughly equivalent to all the energy contained in a billion stars, over their entire lifetimes. Where does that energy come from? And how is it converted into radio emission? No firm answers yet.

GALACTIC EXPLOSIONS

The sketches on page 121 give the impression that radio galaxies can be arranged into a sequence, a sequence that starts with bright-core sources and moves along to a double source such as Cygnus A, where most of the radio emission is coming from far outside the galaxy's visible body.

It is tempting to speculate that this sequence shows a history of explosions in the cores of galaxies. In 1943, C. K. Seyfert (1911–60) called attention to the fact that some spiral galaxies have unusually bright cores. The so-called *Seyfert galaxies* contain considerable loose gas, highly excited and moving with velocities of some 4500 km/sec. Twenty years later Allan R. Sandage of Mt. Palomar in California and C. R. Lynds (born 1928) of the National Radio Astron-

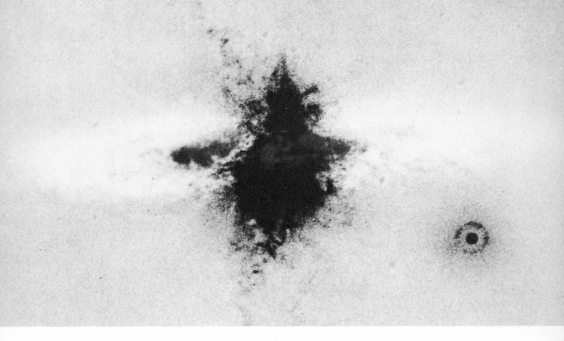

M 82, a galaxy that is exploding. The light areas are the main body of the galaxy, photographed in normal light. The dark region shows vast jets of gas, photographed in the light produced by ionized hydrogen and reproduced here in a negative print for contrast. The explosion filaments are roughly fourteen thousand light years long and are moving with velocities of about 1000 km/sec (Mount Wilson and Palomar Observatories)

omy Observatory in West Virginia provided conclusive evidence in 1963 that galaxies do explode.

Working together, Sandage and Lynds focused their attention on M 82, an irregular galaxy about ten million light years away from earth. Despite its relative nearness, the galaxy is just a hazy patch of light since no stars can be resolved in M 82. It is a moderate radio source.

Sandage and Lynds studied the light produced by ionized hydrogen, which is often the key to the most energetic processes taking place in a galaxy. M 82 had not been carefully surveyed in this manner before.

They found mammoth filaments of hydrogen shooting out of the galaxy at speeds of up to 1000 km/sec and extending for distances of some fourteen thousand light years from the core. The radio emission from M 82 was found to be coming mainly from the core itself and the outflung filaments.

It seemed certain that M 82 had exploded. Judging from the length of the filaments and their velocities, the explosion took place about one and a half million years earlier, or eleven and a half million years ago, because the light we see now from M 82 took ten million years to reach us. But the explosion as Sandage and Lynds saw it—as we see it today— is one and a half million years old.

Are core explosions, then, a natural event in the history of a galaxy? And what of the Milky Way's own radio halo? Is it the result of an explosion at the core of our galaxy? The halo is about one hundred thousand light years from the center of the Milky Way. If it were caused by an explosion, it must have happened more than a million years ago. What was the effect on earth?

Sandage and others estimated the energy needed to produce M 82's explosion to be at least 2×10^{55} ergs. This is equivalent to the energy released by twenty thousand supernovas. Just as in the case of the radio galaxies, no satisfactory answers have come forth about how this energy is produced. But at least we are getting close to understanding the energy of the quasars.

How are the radio galaxies and exploding galaxies related to the quasars? If they are related at all. Do galactic explosions provide a mechanism for explaining the quasars? Some astronomers think so. But others feel that there is no relation, that the quasars are not even galaxy-sized objects.

6

To the Curtain
of Light

...it is more important
to have beauty in one's equations
than to have
them fit experiment.

P.A.M. Dirac

P. A. M. DIRAC (BORN 1902) IS ONE OF THE WORLD'S FOREMOST theoretical physicists. The quotation above is an extreme view of the importance of theoretical work as compared to experiment. In cosmology, however, theory holds the center stage.

Astronomy is hardly an experimental science. That is, even though spacecraft are making experiments within the solar system practical, astronomers are in no position to perform experiments on the stars or galaxies.

Instead of experiments, astronomy depends on observation. Theories are necessary to interpret the observations, to give meaning to the data obtained. A good theory can take dozens of scattered and perhaps confusing observations and bring them together into a single, coherent concept. Even more important, a good theory can predict new facts and show the observers what to look for next. Thus theory and observation work together to bring order and understanding.

Cosmology is the study of the universe as a whole. The observed data in this largest of all possible fields are shockingly scanty. True, everything that is known about the stars and galaxies, about atoms and energy, plays a role in cosmology. But observations that encompass the universe itself, that take in the whole sweep of the heavens instead of its separate parts, these kinds of observations are rare.

In effect, cosmology consists of a few striking observations and a wealth of theories that tries to explain them: a detective story in which only a few clues have been uncovered. The quasars may be one of the truly important clues that will turn out to be "eye witnesses" to the very beginning of the universe.

THE REDSHIFTED GALAXIES

All of modern cosmology is built on one basic observation: the redshifts of the outer galaxies, discovered by Hubble in 1929. Several astronomers played a role in this discovery, including V. M. Slipher (born 1875) and Milton L. Humason (born 1891), both Americans; but Hubble was the central figure.

The redshift is assumed to be caused by the motion of the galaxies away from the Milky Way. The nearest galaxies, the members of the Local Group, are not all moving away from us. They appear to be moving rather at random, some approaching the Milky Way and some receding. But the farther galaxies are all redshifted, and the greater the galaxy's distance from us, the greater its redshift.

The redshift is assumed to be a *Doppler shift*. Christian

Doppler (1803–53), an Austrian mathematical physicist, suggested in 1842 that light should shift toward the red if the source of the light is moving away from the observer, and toward the blue if the light is approaching.

But are the redshifts of the galaxies really Doppler shifts? There are two other theories: the redshift may be caused by gravitational forces or by the absorption of light by gas or dust in intergalactic space.

The gravitational theory has a solid basis in physical fact. When light waves leave an object as massive as a star, they must do work to escape. This causes them to shift toward the lower-energy end of the spectrum, which is the red end. Most scientists believe, however, that gravitational forces cannot produce the large shifts observed in the galaxies. Moreover, it would be difficult to explain the increasing redshifts of the more distant galaxies as due to gravitational forces; after all, the galaxies are assumed to be of roughly the same size and mass, despite their distances from us.

The second theory states that the light from the galaxies is being absorbed by gas or dust between them, just as starlight inside the Milky Way is partially absorbed and reddened by interstellar dust. This effect could nicely explain the increase of redshift with increasing distance; more distance means more absorption. But observation shows that there is probably far too little gas (and perhaps no dust at all) in intergalactic space to account for the redshifts.

As Dirac pointed out, these observations may be in error, and one of these theories may be right. But until more observational evidence comes in, only the Doppler theory agrees fully with what has been seen.

In line with the Doppler theory, then, the outer galaxies are all moving away from us; the farther they are, the faster their speed of recession. But this, too, is derived theoretically:

the only thing that is actually measured is the redshift.

No one is suggesting that the Milky Way is the center of the universe, even though it appears that all the outer galaxies are hurrying away from us. If we could be transported to a distant galaxy and look at the sky from there, it would seem that our new galaxy is standing still and all the others— including the Milky Way—are rushing away. The entire universe, then, is believed to be expanding.

One way to picture this expansion is to imagine a balloon speckled with dots. As the balloon is inflated, each dot moves farther away from the other dots. To a thinking microbe on one dot, it would seem as though his dot were at rest and all the others were moving away. But his dot is moving, too. In fact the very fabric of his universe—the balloon's skin —is expanding.

And so is the fabric of our universe expanding, according to modern cosmological theory.

Interestingly, clusters of galaxies are holding together and moving as groups. Gravitational forces that bind clusters to- gether are stronger than the force causing the expansion. Even as small a cluster as the Local Group is not breaking up; it is moving as a group in the general expansion of the universe.

THE SIZE AND AGE OF THE UNIVERSE

How are the redshifts equated to distance? Individual Cepheid variable stars can be resolved in the closest galaxies —even a few outside the Local Group. The distances to these galaxies are measured by timing the Cepheids and comparing their calculated luminosity to their observed magnitudes. In the rest of the galaxies, though, individual stars cannot be seen. However, these galaxies are smaller and fainter than the Cepheid-measured galaxies and are therefore presumably farther away.

Hubble and others noted that the smaller and fainter a galaxy appears the greater its redshift. If the redshift is truly a Doppler shift, then the larger redshifts mean greater speeds of recession. Theoretical work that was going on at the same time as Hubble's observations supported the idea that the universe is expanding. If it is expanding, then the farther a galaxy is from us, the faster its speed of recession ought to be. Thus the redshifts should be an indication of distance. This relationship of recession velocity and distance is shown in the diagram below.

Figure 14. The relation of redshift to distance for the farthest known galaxies (not including the quasars). The redshift is presumed to be a measure of the galaxy's speed of recession and is used to estimate the distance of the galaxy. If the universe originated in a single primitive explosion, more distant galaxies should fall along the upper curve (BB). If the universe has always been as it is now, with no definite beginning, the farther galaxies should follow the curve labeled SS. If the quasars are actually extremely distant galaxies, they could help to determine which theory of the origin of the universe is correct

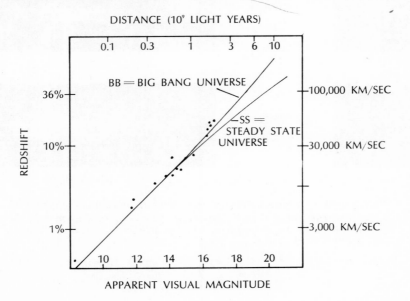

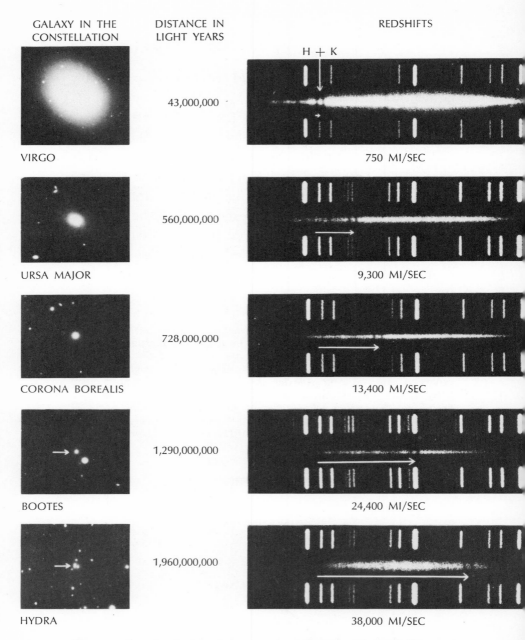

GALAXY IN THE CONSTELLATION	DISTANCE IN LIGHT YEARS	REDSHIFTS
VIRGO	43,000,000	750 MI/SEC
URSA MAJOR	560,000,000	9,300 MI/SEC
CORONA BOREALIS	728,000,000	13,400 MI/SEC
BOOTES	1,290,000,000	24,400 MI/SEC
HYDRA	1,960,000,000	38,000 MI/SEC

H + K

Photographs of galaxies, their spectra, and their estimated distances. Note that the smaller and dimmer a galaxy is, the greater is the redshift of its spectrum, and hence the greater is its presumed distance (Mount Wilson and Palomar Observatories)

The redshift is measured by comparing the spectrum of a galaxy with spectra produced in the laboratory by known light sources, at rest. The astronomer finds that the spectral lines in the galaxy's spectrum are not in the same places as those of his "rest source."

The redshift can be expressed in several ways.

First, it can be given as the difference between the shifted and unshifted ("rest") wavelengths of the spectral line being considered. For example, in M 87, one of the spectral lines of calcium is shifted from a rest wavelength of 3933.664 Å to 3950.792 Å, a shift of 0.4 percent.

The measured redshift can be translated into the galaxy's velocity of recession, and this velocity can then be expressed as a percentage of the speed of light. For M 87, the recession velocity has been calculated to be some 1200 km/sec, which is just about 0.4 percent of the speed of light.

When the velocity of recession is known, the distance can be calculated from the formula $V = Hr$, where V is the galaxy's velocity, r is the distance, and H is a special factor called the *Hubble constant*. This calculation yields a distance of about 12 megaparsecs for M 87.

The Hubble constant is needed in the equation because the galaxies are not all moving at the same rate, so their distances are not dependent on their velocities alone. At present, the Hubble constant is believed to be between 70 and 150 km/sec for each megaparsec of distance. That is, a galaxy at 50 megaparsecs is moving 70 to 150 km/sec faster than a galaxy at 49 megaparsecs' distance.

All this makes the estimation of distances to the farthest galaxies quite tricky. But it is the best that can be done. Table 2 shows some of the redshift measurements and resulting distance estimates for the farthest known galaxy and a few quasars. The distance estimates are based on the assumption that the redshifts are caused by the expansion of the universe.

Incidentally, the spectrograms of the galaxies are usually made on photographic film that is only 15 mm (⅝ inch) long. Thus the distances to the farthest galaxies are actually measured in a microscope!

Shaky though it is, this technique of judging distances by redshifts can yield an estimate of the size of the whole observable universe.

For simplicity's sake, assume that the Hubble constant is 100 km/sec per megaparsec. Knowing that the farther an object is the faster it is receding, we can calculate how far a galaxy would be if it were moving at the speed of light, 3×10^5 km/sec. This distance works out to be roughly 3000 megaparsecs (3 billion parsecs, or 3 *giga*parsecs).

This gives a rough—very rough—idea of how far we should expect to be able to see into space. Since the whole procedure is based on the inexact Hubble constant and other not-fully-proven assumptions, the "size" should be taken as nothing more than a gross approximation.

Furthermore, Einstein showed that no object in the universe can move as fast as light; therefore we will never find a galaxy 3 gigaparsecs away. And even more: as a galaxy begins to reach a velocity close to light speed, relativity theory shows that its light begins to fade. So if there are galaxies moving at nearly light speed, we won't see them.

In effect, there's a "curtain of light" around us at a distance of somewhat closer than 3000 megaparsecs. Beyond that, we can't hope to observe anything. The *observable universe* lies within this radius. There may be more galaxies and worlds beyond, but we are not able to observe them.

If the expansion of the universe is taken to mean that all the galaxies originally began at a certain place and then flew apart, we can estimate how long ago they began their journeys by backtracking them. If we divide the distance of any galaxy by its recession velocity, we get roughly the same answer, no matter which galaxy we choose: about ten billion years.

Is that the age of the universe?

DRAWING THE BIG PICTURE

For nearly forty years all of cosmology has hung on the single thread of the redshift. The major question has been: if the universe is expanding, what is causing the expansion?

This leads to a special part of cosmology, called *cosmogony*, or the study of the origin of the universe. Inevitably, cosmologists have tried not only to grasp the nature of the universe as it exists today, but they are trying to understand how it originated, as well.

Like so much of modern physical science, our current ideas about cosmology and cosmogony were triggered by Albert Einstein (1879–1955). In 1917 he published his thoughts on what the universe must look like, in the light of his concept of relativity. Without going into details on relativity theory, we can simply state that Einstein's universe exists in space that is curved, not flat as previous thinking had assumed. The Einstein universe was spherical, with the galaxies in it delicately balanced between gravitational attraction that tended to pull them together, and a "cosmic repulsion" force that tended to push them apart. (Remember, this was a dozen years before the discovery of the redshifts!) The net effect, as Einstein saw it, was an essentially static universe; the galaxies were neither flying apart nor falling together.

The Russian mathematician Alexander Friedmann pointed out, though, that Einstein's universe was unstable. It could so easily be pushed into either a general expansion or a general collapse that it was hard to believe Einstein was describing the universe as it really existed.

Hubble's announcement of the redshifts, of course, tipped the scales in favor of expansion. But it is important to realize that by the time the redshift was discovered, the theoreticians were already looking for evidence of a dynamic universe— either expanding or contracting.

In 1931, Georges Lemaitre, the Belgian priest-cosmologist (born 1894) put forth a theory to explain how the expansion of the universe began.

Lemaitre pictured all the matter and energy of the universe —all the stuff of the galaxies and stars, all their radiation energy, everything—packed into a single enormously dense package about thirty times the size of the sun. Lemaitre called this the "primeval atom." In such an enormously tight squeeze, matter as we know it could not exist. Even atoms would be broken down into smaller particles. The density of the primeval atom would be so high that a cubic centimeter of its substance would contain one hundred million tons of matter.

The primitive atom exploded, and the fragments eventually turned into the atoms and stars and galaxies and people and everything else that we know today. The expansion of the universe, then, is the result of this original explosion. The galaxies can be thought of as celestial shrapnel, still flying outward.

THE BIG BANG

George Gamow (1904–68), a Russian-born American physicist and cosmologist, elaborated on Lemaitre's ideas and brought the power of nuclear physics into cosmology. Starting in 1946 (the year after the first nuclear bombs were exploded), Gamow became the best-known spokesman for what has become known as the *Big Bang* theory of the universe's origin.

Gamow borrowed an ancient Greek word for primeval matter and called the original stuff of the universe *ylem* (pronounced EYE-lem). Like Lemaitre's primeval atom, the ylem is pictured as highly condensed. But Gamow worked out a sequence of reactions which, he believed, showed in detail how the atoms that we know today—from hydrogen to uranium and beyond—were created in the Big Bang.

The ylem consisted of neutrons and radiant energy, according to Gamow. Some ten billion years ago, the ylem exploded with a cosmic blast of light and energy. At the time of the explosion the temperature of the ylem must have been billions of degrees: this can be calculated from the assumed density and known physical laws.

As the explosion hurled the ylem outward, the density, and hence the temperature, began to drop drastically. After about five minutes, the density was low enough for the ylem to have cooled down to about 100 million degrees. At this temperature, neutrons begin to spontaneously change into protons and electrons. (This has been observed in nuclear physics laboratories; the mechanisms and conditions for neutron "decay" are well understood.)

Where neutrons, protons, and electrons are all intermingled with huge amounts of radiant energy, the particles will begin to interact. Gamow proposed that the particles combined to form the atoms of the various elements: a proton and electron combining to form a hydrogen atom; two protons, two neutrons, and two electrons coalescing into a helium atom; and so forth, all the way up to the heaviest elements.

Gamow was able to make a good match between the known abundances of the elements in the universe and the rate of element-forming action in the earliest stages of the ylem explosion. He proposed that all the elements were produced in the first half-hour of the Big Bang. While this speed may seem fantastic at first glance, Gamow was able to show that it corresponded to the speed of nuclear reactions that take place in nuclear bomb explosions.

For some thirty million years the atoms continued to expand from the original source of the explosion, and the temperature of the universe declined steadily. At about the thirty-million-year point, the temperature had dropped to 300°K (about room temperature). At this point, the atoms could begin to come together and combine. The universe was a dark, though humanely warm, thin gas. Gravitational forces and the natural behavior of gases now began to break up this smooth cloud into separate clumps of gas. Eventually, galaxy-sized clouds were produced and star formation began. For the first time since the original explosion, light shone in the void once more.

Gamow's theory accounted for nearly everything, although the details of galaxy formation are still far from understood.

But there was a hitch. Gamow's theory required a smooth buildup of the elements from the lightest to the heaviest. Studies showed that this could not happen under the conditions postulated for the ylem explosion. The best that could be done in the Big Bang was to produce hydrogen and helium. No further element formation could take place, according to the majority of astrophysicists. The joke that "Gamow's theory is a wonderful way to build the elements all the way up to helium" made the rounds of the world's universities.

THE STEADY-STATE UNIVERSE

Meanwhile, a group of British cosmologists were offering a strikingly different view of the universe. It got around Gamow's problems of element building, but it has difficulties of its own.

In 1948, Hermann Bondi, Thomas Gold, and Fred Hoyle (born 1919, 1920, and 1915, respectively) announced their *Steady-State* theory. Their ideas hit the astronomical-cosmological world with the force of a revolution. Hoyle, like Gamow, is an excellent writer who writes well for the layman; hence he is the most widely known of the Steady-State proponents.

The Steady-State theory depicts the universe as having no beginning and no end. Individual stars and galaxies are born, go through life cycles, and die out; but they are replaced by new stars and galaxies. The universe goes on, and looks pretty much the same regardless of time.

In the Big Bang cosmology, the density of the universe is steadily decreasing with time, and the universe is said to be *evolving*. In the Steady-State universe, the density is always the same and the universe is not evolving. The galaxies are not more thickly packed today than they will be ten billion years from now; nor were they more thickly clustered ten billion years ago than they are now.

Then what causes the expansion of the universe? The

Steady-State cosmology calls for the spontaneous creation of new matter—probably in the form of individual hydrogen atoms. This new matter is created out of nothing, and no cause for its creation is given by the theory. It simply pops into being in space, at a rate high enough to force the universe to expand to make room for the new material coming in. Originally the theory called for one new hydrogen atom to come into being in a space of about 250 cubic meters every 250 million years. Gamow was prompted to remark, "the creative genie would not over-strain himself doing the job."

The Steady-State theory met strong criticism because of its "something for nothing" assumption of the spontaneous creation of matter. This repelled most scientists for philosophical reasons. All cosmogonic theories, however, eventually face a blank wall when considering where the matter and energy of the universe originated. Where did the ylem or primeval atom come from? There is no attempt at an answer; it is merely there. Is it so different to say that it is merely there, one atom at a time, continuously, instead of everything all at once?

The Steady-State theory did successfully account for the creation of the elements heavier than hydrogen by showing that they are "cooked" inside of stars during their main sequence and red giant phases and during stellar explosions. This idea is fully accepted and accounts for the evolutionary tracks of the stars. It was first proposed as part of the Steady-State theory.

THE WEIGHT OF EVIDENCE: QUASARS AND "SNOW"

There is a simple observational test that could decide which of the two major cosmological theories are correct. The Big

Bang theory states that the galaxies were more densely packed together eons ago, while the Steady-State theory claims that they were not.

When we look at the distant galaxies, we see light that has taken millions upon millions of years to reach us. In effect, we're seeing them as they were ages ago. For example, we see the sun as it existed eight minutes ago, because it is eight light minutes away. We see M 31 as it was some two million years ago, since it is about two million light years distant. And we may be seeing the quasars as they were ten billion years ago—which is about the time of the original Big Bang!

For more than twenty years astronomers have been trying to determine whether the farthest galaxies are more closely packed together than are those near the Milky Way. The observations are difficult to make, and the distant galaxies— even those a billion or two light years away—are simply not far enough to make a clear-cut decision.

But the quasars are. That is, if they are really distant objects.

Are the quasars more densely grouped than the closer galaxies? This is not a simple question, and with only a few hundred quasars clearly identified as such, compared to billions of galaxies, perhaps it is the wrong question to ask. But the strong radio sources, which include known radio galaxies, quasars, and sources for which no optical identification has been made (possibly because the sources are too far away to be seen), are apparently more densely clustered than the nearer galaxies.

Hoyle has concluded reluctantly that, "The indication of the radio counts is that the universe was more dense in the past than it is today." He quickly points out, however, that if the quasars and the yet unidentified radio sources are not at cosmological distances, but are really fairly close to the Milky Way, then the Steady-State theory may still hold up.

But another point of evidence has dealt the Steady-State theory a serious blow. You see this evidence sometimes on your own television screen.

The original Big Bang (if there was one) hurled radiation energy, as well as matter, outward. Calculations have shown that this energy, although fallen to a very low temperature over ten billion years, should still be emitting faint radio waves that can be detected by suitable receivers.

In 1967, two groups of researchers at Bell Telephone Laboratories and Princeton University announced that they had detected faint signals at wavelengths of 7.35 and 3.2 cm; other groups picked up radiation at 20.7 and 2.6 cm. The nature of the radiation is such that most scientists are satisfied it is coming from the remnants of the primeval "fireball" of the Big Bang. This so-called *fireball radiation* causes some of the annoying "snow" that occasionally clouds television reception.

Steady-State proponents have pointed out, however, that this low-energy radiation could be coming from causes other than the primeval fireball.

In balance, though, the weight of the evidence points strongly toward the Big Bang version about the origin of the universe, although the Steady-State concept of "cooking" the elements in the stars has become a firmly accepted part of astrophysics and cosmology.

The matter rests largely on the quasars. Are they really billions of light years away? If they are not, then perhaps many of the unidentified radio sources are also much closer than they are now believed to be. If that is true, then the evidence that the universe was denser eons ago evaporates, and there is still no clear-cut choice between the Big Bang and the Steady-State.

Furthermore, Hoyle has another possibility in mind. Understandably reluctant to give up entirely on the Steady-State theory, he believes that even if the quasars are out at the edge of the known universe, they may be something very different from galaxies: "perhaps the quasars are an indication that the universe has lots of little bangs instead of one big bang, little bangs that are nevertheless far more violent than the gentle processes [originally proposed by] the Steady-State theory."

ANTIMATTER AND THE OSCILLATING UNIVERSE

There is still a nagging question. Where did the ylem, the original stuff of the universe, come from? Was there a time when even it did not exist? How did it come into being, then?

Perhaps no human cosmology will ever answer that question. With our observational tools and our theories, we can probe only so far into space and time. It appears as if we can never hope to understand how the primeval matter and energy of the universe originated.

Many cosmologists have sought to get around this uncomfortable question by suggesting that the universe goes through an endless cycle of oscillations: ylem, explosion, expansion out to a certain point, then contraction, the universe falls back into ylem once more, then a new explosion and expansion . . . *ad infinitum, seculae secularum.*

This concept of an oscillating universe is not very different from the basic principle of the Steady-State cosmology: the universe had no beginning and will have no end. It merely oscillates back and forth, expansion phase and contraction phase. If you take a truly stupendous time scale, long enough to cover many expansions and contractions (each of which may last tens of billions of years), then perhaps you can say that the universe is in a sort of dynamic steady-state, after all.

But there is another factor, a factor that may have an important bearing on the quasar mystery.

We know that atoms are made up of neutrons, protons, electrons, and many other subatomic particles that have been discovered in high-energy physics experiments. For each type of particle there is an *antiparticle*—a type of particle that can be thought of as a mirror twin of the proton, electron, or neutron.

It was Dirac who, in 1931, first postulated the existence of an antielectron. He predicted that it would look like an electron except that its electrical charge would be positive instead of negative. The next year, antielectrons were found in the course of an experiment deliberately set up to produce them.

The antielectron was named the *positron*, short for positive electron. In time, antiprotons, antineutrons, and antiparticles for all the "normal" particles of nuclear physics were discovered.

Antimatter, material composed of antiparticles, reacts violently with "normal" matter. When a particle and antiparticle meet, they annihilate each other; the matter is turned into energy. The nuclear fusion of hydrogen into helium converts only 0.7 percent of the original matter into energy. Matter-antimatter annihilation is much more energetic: *all* of the reacting mass can be converted into energy.

Physicists were faced with a puzzle. Why should the universe consist only of matter? Shouldn't antimatter be present in just as much abundance as "normal" matter? The unavoidable answer is, yes; there is no reason for nature to prefer our type of matter to antimatter. In fact, the stars and galaxies could just as well be antimatter, for all we know. It would take precise observations, calling for equipment beyond our abilities to build, to tell from earth whether a particular star is antimatter or not. Actually, until spacecraft touched down on the moon, we had no way of telling if it was matter or antimatter.

The Swedish physicists Oscar Klein and Hannes Alfven (born 1894 and 1908, respectively) have considered the cosmological implications of antimatter. Klein and Alfven describe the universe as made equally of matter and antimatter. If the universe oscillates, then, when it contracts, it reaches a high enough density for collisions between the atoms and antiatoms to provide the energy to force an expansion. During the expansion phase, the matter and antimatter become separated again, not to meet until the next contraction phase forces them together. In the Big Bang, then, particles form hydrogen and helium, which eventually builds stars and galaxies; while antiparticles form antihydrogen and antihelium, which builds antistars and antigalaxies. And the energy of the Big Bang itself comes from the mutual annihilation of matter and antimatter.

Is the matter and antimatter completely separated during the expansion phase? No, the regions where they are not separated would be ablaze with their mutual annihilation. Klein and Alfven visualize these regions as a sort of cosmic battlefront, violent with the blaze of matter-antimatter collisions, where the particles are flashed into energy. Behind these battlefronts the "civilian populations" of galaxies and antigalaxies, gas clouds and antigas clouds, live peacefully among their own kind.

Could the quasars be these battle zones, where matter and antimatter are meeting in mutual annihilation? Many astrophysicists have pointed out that only something as violent as a matter-antimatter collision could explain the apparent energy output of the quasars.

7

A Closer Look
at the Quasars

...a riddle wrapped in
a mystery inside an enigma

Winston Churchill

IF CHURCHILL HAD DELIBERATELY TRIED TO GIVE A THUMBNAIL
description of our current knowledge of the quasars, he
couldn't have done better than the line quoted above.

In Chapter 1 we briefly reviewed the events that led up
to the discovery of the quasars. In the chapters that fol-
lowed, we looked at the workings of the stars and galaxies
and examined the theoretical framework of cosmology. We
can understand now just how important the quasars are to
astronomy and cosmology. If the quasars are truly the farthest
objects yet found, they are extremely important to man's
understanding of the universe.

Throughout the first six chapters, we also became
acquainted with the tools and techniques of modern astronomy—optical and radio telescopes, spectroscopy, distance
measurements, redshift measurements, and so on. We can
begin to see how these tools are being used by astronomers to

examine the enigmatic, mysterious riddle of the quasars.

In this chapter we will build up as complete a picture as possible of what the quasars look like. Astronomers have put together a considerable body of evidence. But there are gaps, many unanswered questions. Much of the observational evidence can be interpreted in several different ways, and the theorists are split into different camps when it comes to explaining how the quasars fit into the scheme of the universe.

JARGON AGAIN

We know that light and radio waves are both electromagnetic waves. Wavelength is the measure of the distance between waves: for example, the distance from the crest of one wave to the crest of the next one. Light waves have wavelengths of less than 10^{-4} mm, while the radio waves used in astronomy are between 1 cm and 20 meters in wavelength.

Radio astronomers usually work and think in terms of *frequency*, rather than wavelength. The frequency of a particular wave is defined as the number of those waves that pass a given point in a given time (usually one second). Figure 15 compares wavelengths and frequencies for the part of the electromagnetic spectrum that we are interested in. The shorter the wavelength, the higher the frequency. Low-frequency waves have long wavelengths and vice versa.

Radio astronomers speak in terms of "megacycles per second" (Mc/sec) or just "megacycles" with the "per second" understood; Mc/sec is a frequency of a million waves per second. Increasingly, though, the term *Hertz* is being used to replace cycles per second, so that radio people now often say "megahertz" in place of megacycle.

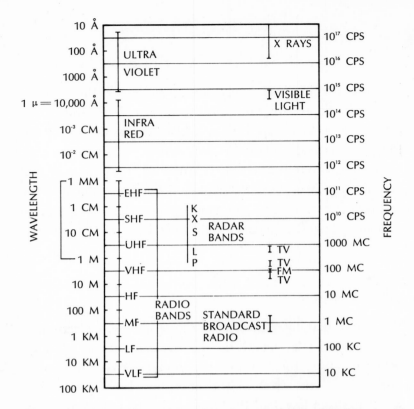

Figure 15. The relation of wavelength to frequency for the part of the electromagnetic spectrum used in astronomy, radio broadcasting, television, and radar. The term Hertz is often used in place of cycles per second

SPOTTING THE QUASARS

Quasars have been photographed for nearly eighty years, but until about 1963 no one realized that some of the faint-looking blue "stars" in the sky are far more than meets the casual eye—or camera.

But how do you identify a quasar? How is a quasar's appearance different from a star's or galaxy's?

Quasars have no single characteristic that immediately identifies them. But they do exhibit a combination of characteristics that clearly distinguishes them from ordinary stars and galaxies.

Among these characteristic traits of the quasars are

1. A starlike visual appearance
2. Often (but not always) strong radio emission
3. Strong inherent ultraviolet radiation
4. Large redshift
5. Variable light and/or radio output

The quasars look like stars, not galaxies. The brightest quasar, 3C 273, has an apparent optical magnitude of 12.8; the dimmest quasars yet discovered are around m = 20. Most known quasars are between m = 15 to 18. At these magnitudes, a galaxy looks different from a star: spiral galaxies appear spindle-shaped, ellipticals look fuzzy. While some of the quasars look slightly fuzzy, as though there are gas clouds around them, and some—like 3C 273—have jets streaking out from them, most of them are clearly different in appearance from galaxies.

Many of the quasars are strong radio emitters, but an increasing number of radio-quiet quasars are being discovered. Strong radio emission was the key to the original discovery of the quasars, but radio-quiet quasars lack this feature.

All the quasars, regardless of their radio performance, appear to be blue objects, putting out a large fraction of their total energy emission in the ultraviolet wavelengths. (Most UV radiation is absorbed by our atmosphere and cannot reach the ground.) Because of the quasars' large redshifts, however, we can detect much of this light, since it is shifted downward to wavelengths that can be seen through the earth's atmosphere.

This blueness of the quasars combined with a large redshift is a prime hallmark. Several estimates have been made of the total number of quasars that might be in the heavens, based on the number discovered so far and the total number of blue

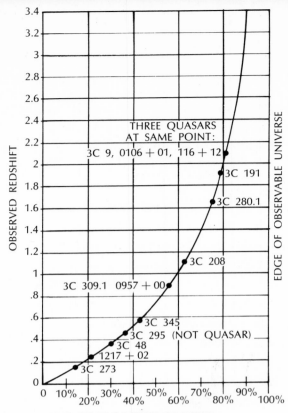

Figure 16. *The observed redshifts of several quasars and the galaxy 3C 295. The curve shows how the redshift is related to the speed of the object's motion away from us, based on the assumption that the redshifts are due to the expansion of the universe. Thus the galaxy 3C 295 is believed to be the farthest known galaxy, while quasars such as 3C 9 are much farther away and presumably moving at more than 80 percent of the speed of light*

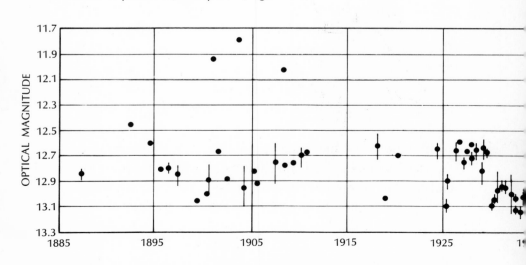

starlike objects known to exist. It could be that there are some forty thousand quasars, or one for every square degree of the sky, considering only those objects that are fainter than m = 15. This is an estimate, however, and it is only as good as the assumptions that went into it.

Another clear clue to the presence of a quasar is variable energy output. Some stars vary in their light emission, and a few galaxies have been found to have variable radio emission. The quasars vary in both light and radio output, and the fluctuations can take place in amazingly short times.

The most studied of the quasars is 3C 273 since it is the brightest (m = 12.8) and therefore the easiest to observe. It has been photographed since about 1885, as part of routine sky survey work. The plot below shows the variations in light output of 3C 273 over nearly eighty years based on photos at Harvard College Observatory.

As the plot shows, 3C 273 has varied by about 1.5 magnitudes. Occasional "flashes" of increased brightness have come and gone inside of a month. Its radio output also fluctuates strongly. At 8000 Mc/sec its radio "brightness" is increasing by nearly 20 percent per year. Radio output at lower frequencies is also getting stronger. In the microwave region of the

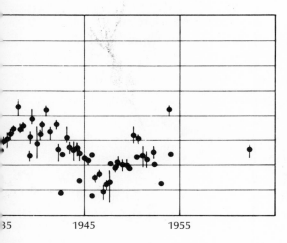

Figure 17. The quasar 3C 273 has been photographed for nearly eighty years, although it was not until the 1960s that it was realized to be anything but a faint blue star. This plot shows how the brightness of 3C 273 has fluctuated over the years as determined from photographs taken at Harvard College Observatory

35   1945   1955

spectrum, at a wavelength of 3.4 mm, 3C 273 shows significant changes over periods as short as a few weeks.

The quasar 3C 345, although nearly forty times dimmer (m = 16.8) than 3C 273, is much more spectacular. Over a twenty-day period in the summer of 1965 it increased in optical brightness by nearly half a magnitude, then started to grow dimmer. Its brightness fluctuated every few days, even though the overall trend of its light output was downward. Then, between the beginning and end of October 1965, its optical brightness jumped again by a full magnitude.

The "high jump" record is held by 3C 446: its optical brightness increased two full magnitudes in just ten days during July 1966. And it has been seen to vary by half to eight-tenths of a magnitude over twenty-four hours. The "speed" record was set by 3C 48 in 1961, when it jumped 0.04 magnitude inside of fifteen minutes!

These variations pose a staggering problem for anyone trying to determine just what the quasars are and how they work. Only small, dim flare stars have shown comparable magnitude changes, and their light output is some 10^{11} to 10^{15} lower than the quasars'.

The quasars identified so far seem to have a curious distribution in the sky. Radio galaxies are spread across the heavens rather evenly; there seem to be no more in any one direction than in any other. But this is decidedly not so for the quasars.

Most of the quasars have been found at high galactic latitudes. That is, if you were to draw a map of the Milky Way, most quasars would appear close to the galaxy's north and south poles. Comparatively few have been found closer to the galactic equator than 40° (see the drawing on page 151). We are talking about the quasars' positions as though they were points of light tacked onto a dome-shaped sky.

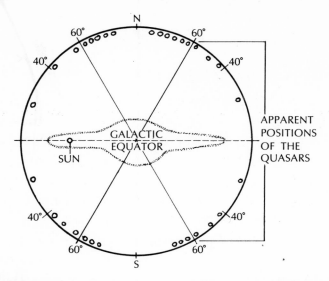

Figure 18. *The positions of the quasars in the sky seem to be clustered somewhat around the polar regions of the Milky Way. This says nothing about their distances; they may be near the Milky Way or farther than any known galaxy. But most of them are found within 40° of the poles of the Milky Way*

It is their *positions* in the sky that we are discussing, not their distances. They could be close to the Milky Way or out at the edge of the universe; no one knows for certain. But their positions in the sky are clustered around the Milky Way's poles.

Why is this so? Some astronomers feel that this distribution is an important clue to the nature of the quasars; others insist that the distribution is illusory, caused by observational limitations, and the quasars are really spread equally all over the sky.

It is true that interstellar dust hampers the observation of galaxies along the Milky Way's equator (Hubble's "zone of avoidance"). It is equally true that there are few observatories in the southern hemisphere that can make redshift measurements and spot new quasars.

But despite these limitations in observational capabilities, most astronomers now agree that quasars seem to "prefer" high galactic latitudes; they are actually grouped near the Milky Way's north and south poles.

Halton C. Arp (born 1927) of the Carnegie Institute of Washington and California Institute of Technology has brought out additional evidence about the quasars' locations. He has shown that radio sources generally lie within a few degrees of a "peculiar" galaxy. A peculiar galaxy in this sense means one that shows a complex structure, such as Cygnus A, or is otherwise puzzling or unusual, such as the exploding M 82 and the Seyfert galaxies.

Many radio galaxies have two radio emission regions placed symmetrically on either side of the visually observable galaxy. Arp and others have gone farther and claimed that quasars and even full-scale radio galaxies are usually found close to a peculiar galaxy.

Does the evidence of the quasars' clustering around the Milky Way's poles mean that they were ejected from our galaxy? Does Arp's evidence mean that quasars—and perhaps whole galaxies—are formed of material ejected from peculiar galaxies? We shall consider these questions in the next chapter.

HOW BIG IS A QUASAR?

Radio and optical astronomers have worked hard to determine the sizes of the quasars.

Optically, of course, the quasars appear small enough to have long been mistaken for stars in our own galaxy. When the 200-inch Mt. Palomar telescope is turned on them, they reveal some structure. Many of them seem to be enmeshed in hazy gas clouds; several show jets of bright matter extending from the main body. In all of them, though, there is a small, intensely bright core.

The same situation applies for the radio studies. At different frequencies, the quasars show different angular dimensions. This is not surprising since most radio sources are this way. It merely means that certain radio frequencies are being emitted from specific parts of the source. If you tune in one frequency, you receive a signal from one region; another frequency will reveal a different region, perhaps deeper inside the source.

Every quasar reveals a small core at the heart of the radio source where most of the radio energy originates. This radio core is not necessarily the same as the optical core, although precise locations of such small angular dimensions are difficult to nail down with certainty.

Typically, quasar cores are found to be less than 0."5, with many smaller than 0."1. Unfortunately, these angular dimensions cannot be translated into physical sizes—in kilometers or light years or whatever—unless we know the distances of the quasars.

But there is another way to guess at the sizes of the quasars. This method depends on their fluctuations in brightness.

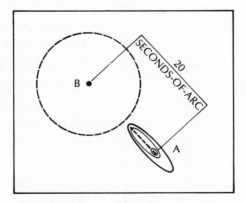

Figure 19. The radio structure of 3C 273. Radio energy from component A comes from several regions, while radio emission from B comes from an intense but very small core

Modern physics is based on Einstein's principle that nothing can move faster than light. Whatever it is that causes the quasars to fluctuate, it presumably starts in one spot and travels across the quasar—or perhaps across a certain part of the quasar: the core, for example. No matter whether the quasar is actually a single object such as a gas cloud, or a collection of stars like a galaxy, the disturbance must start somewhere and travel outward. Its top speed is limited to light speed.

Thus a disturbance that varies a quasar's brightness over a period of 24 hours must cover an area of the quasar that is 24 light-hours wide, at most. Therefore, if a quasar varies in brightness in 24 hours, we can reason that there is a region of the quasar that is no more than 24 light-hours wide, *regardless of how far away the quasar is.*

Most astronomers have equated these brightness changes with the cores of the quasars. Light travels roughly 3×10^{10} kilometers in 24 hours, about three times the diameter of the solar system. In a month, light covers some 10^{12} kilometers, or 100 times the solar system's diameter.

Quasars that show brightness variations over 24 hours presumably have cores only slightly larger than the solar system; brightness changes of a month's duration probably come from regions that are about 10^{12} kilometers wide. Thus, by measuring the period of a quasar's fluctuation in brightness, some idea of its actual size can be established. But that is most likely the size of only a part of the quasar—the core, it is usually assumed. How do these "core sizes" compare with other astronomical bodies?

We have seen that individual stars may be as large as the diameter of Mars' orbit (about 650 million kilometers). Among the largest known single stars is Epsilon Aurigae, with a diameter of nearly 3×10^9 kilometers. But this type of star is dim and of low density; it has been described as "a red hot vacuum." The quasars are much hotter, denser, and fantastically brighter. And their cores are larger by at least a factor of ten than even these most gigantic types of stars. Moreover, the quasar cores are apparently surrounded by considerable additional material, so that the true diameter of the whole quasar is considerably larger than the core.

But while the quasars are much larger than stars, they are without doubt much smaller than galaxies. After all, galactic diameters are measured in light *years*, not light months or days.

There is a chance, though, that the reasoning behind the "fluctuation period-diameter" technique is based on a false assumption. Suppose a large area of a quasar suddenly increased in brightness and, after a day or a month, just as suddenly the whole area decreased its brightness again. There would be no way of telling how large the area is unless you knew the distance to the quasar and the angular dimension of the fluctuating area. There is no reasonable way to imagine how an area—be it a large gas cloud, a single superenormous star, or even a galaxy-sized assembly of stars—could "light up" all at once. It would be something like having half the stars of the Milky Way explode into novas simultaneously. But then not much about the quasars is reasonable!

The simpler explanation, however, is that the brightness fluctuations are caused by some wave of disturbance that travels across the quasar at light speed or slower. Therefore, most astronomers are content to base their estimates of the quasars' core diameters on these fluctuations. Content, but wary. Unproved assumptions must always be watched skeptically.

THE BRIGHTEST LIGHTS OF ALL

The really staggering thing about the quasars—and the most puzzling problem about them—is their power output.

The sun emits 3.8×10^{33} ergs per second, equivalent to the explosive power of 10^{10} megatons of TNT or equal to 3.8×10^{23} kilowatts, roughly 10^{15} times more than all the electricity generated in the United States.

The maddening problem of the quasars' distances bedevils estimates of their power output, of course. All we can measure on earth is the amount of energy our optical and radio telescopes receive. To translate this into the energy actually emitted by the quasars, we must know their distances from us, just as we had to know the sun's distances before we could calculate its energy output.

While we do not know the quasars' distances for sure, most astronomers have been inclined to accept their redshifts as evidence that they are truly far off at the edge of the observable universe. Let's use that conclusion as a starting point, and see where it leads us.

We discussed in Chapter 5 the optical and radio power outputs of various types of galaxies. Table 13 compares the optical and radio luminosities of the Milky Way, as a typical spiral galaxy; M 87, as a very bright giant elliptical galaxy and a strong radio source; Cygnus A, as the strongest type of nonquasar radio source; and a typical quasar.

If the quasars are at cosmological distances (a billion parsecs or more) then their radio outputs are equal to those of the strongest radio galaxies, such as Cygnus A. Their optical luminosities are even higher: 100 times more than the brightest galaxies, and 1000 times greater than the Milky Way's.

TABLE 13: OPTICAL AND RADIO OUTPUT OF GALAXIES AND QUASARS

Source	Optical Output (KW)	Radio Output (KW)
Milky Way	10^{33}	10^{28}
M 87	10^{34}	10^{32}
Cygnus A	10^{33}	10^{35}
Typical Quasar		
— At "Cosmological" Distance	10^{36}	10^{35}
— At "Local" Distance	10^{32}	10^{31}

Since our galaxy is shining with some 100 billion stars, the typical quasar is putting out 100 trillion stars' worth of light! And most of this radiation is apparently coming from a region that is no more than 100 times larger than the solar system!

To pack that much light output into such a small space means that the quasars must have luminosities equal to the intensity of a laser beam, far brighter than any star's luminosity. It is almost impossible to conceive of any method known to science that could provide so much power in such a small volume. This fact, and the problem of the rapidly changing light and radio output, has led some investigators to postulate that the quasars may be "local" objects, about 10 to 100 million parsecs away, or even closer.

Towing the quasars back from the edge of the universe to the region of relatively nearby galaxies, their energy requirements dwindle by at least a factor of 10^4.

At a "local" distance, the typical quasar is calculated to be emitting about one-tenth the light of the Milky Way and radio energy at about the level of the moderately strong radio sources. The problem of explaining where the energy comes from is less difficult, though still impressive. Table 13 shows the energy requirements. The core diameters, as determined by the quasars' fluctuations, remain the same sizes, of course. But it is considerably easier to build theories that need account for only 10^{32} kilowatts in a volume of one light-month's diameter.

Rough estimates of the minimum distance possible for the quasars have been made by looking for *proper motions*; that is, crosswise motions of the quasars. If a star is close enough to us, we can observe its motion across our field of view. Barnard's "Runaway" Star, which is only six light years away, is moving across the sky at 10 arc-seconds per year. The farther away a star is, of course, the less proper motion we see. Motions toward us or away from us can be determined by spectral shifts, which are sensitive to small velocities. But proper motion depends on the star's distance.

We know from their spectral shifts that the quasars are all racing at tremendous velocities. If they are close enough to the Milky Way, we should be able to see some proper motion. They can't all be moving *exactly* in a line away from us, there must be some crosswise motion involved.

But no proper motion whatsoever has been measured for any quasar. The cosmological theorists cite this as proof that the quasars are not local. The local-theory enthusiasts, however, have shown mathematically that this merely means the quasars must be farther than a few megaparsecs away. If they were as close as one megaparsec, and their redshifts truly were due to a motion away from us, then we should be able to detect some proper motion. If the redshifts have nothing to do with motion—if they are caused by gravitational forces, for example—then there is no reason to expect to find proper motions even if the quasars are closer than one megaparsec.

PROFILE OF A QUASAR

What do we know of the physical make-up of the quasars, and what can this tell us about the problems of their distance, origin, and place in cosmology?

On the one hand, the quasars give strong indications of being individual objects, rather than galaxy-like collections of stars. On the other hand, there are some strong similarities between some of the quasars' characteristics and those found in the nuclei of "active" galaxies such as M 87 and the Seyfert galaxies.

To the radio telescopes, quasars are usually indistinguishable from radio galaxies, at first glance. Many quasars are double sources, as are many radio galaxies. Both types of sources are apparently due to synchrotron radiation: the quasars' radio spectra show decided evidence of nonthermal processes, just as the radio galaxies show. The visible light output of at least one quasar (3C 466) has been found to be polarized in very much the same way as the light from M 87's famous jet. This is strong evidence that the light—and therefore the radio emission, no doubt—is due to synchrotron processes.

But there are some important differences between quasars and radio galaxies. The quasars all have small cores; even the double sources have at least one intense, tiny component. And several quasars have radio spectra that are significantly different from radio galaxies. As Figure 20 shows, radio galaxies emit most strongly at low frequencies, and the energy falls off steadily as the frequency increases. This is typical of nonthermal sources. For some quasars, the radio spectra curves

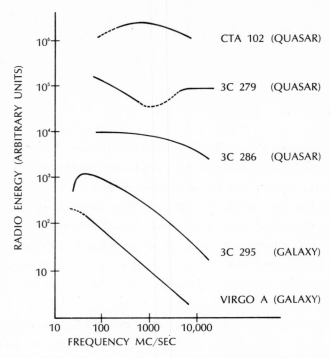

Figure 20. *The radio spectra of quasars do not resemble the spectra of radio galaxies. For radio galaxies, energy output falls off steeply at higher frequencies (shorter wavelengths). Quasar radio spectra are much flatter*

upward again at the high-frequency end. This is still interpreted as a nonthermal spectrum but the physical conditions in the quasar must be such that significant amounts of the radio emission coming from the core are being absorbed by shells of gas surrounding the core.

This "self-absorption" of radio emission and the fact that the quasars show different dimensions at different wavelengths lend strength to the idea that quasar structure is complex. All in all, their radio profiles resemble most closely the radio emissions coming from sources suspected of violent upheavals, such as M 87 and the Seyfert galaxies. Significantly, one of the few nonquasar sources that has shown fluctuations in radio output is the Seyfert galaxy NGC 1275, also known as 3C 84.

Like all Seyfert galaxies, NGC 1275 has a nucleus that is bright with turbulent, agitated gases. This galaxy is relatively nearby, at a distance of 50 megaparsecs. Its nucleus is 0."1 wide, which works out to a diameter of 25 parsecs. The radio fluctuations appear to be coming from a region that is only 0."001 across, or no more than a light year in diameter.

Optical spectra tell much more about the chemical constitution and physical environment of the quasars. They reinforce the notion that the quasars are undergoing violent agitation.

Both emission and absorption lines have been found in quasar optical spectra, with emission lines predominating. The spectra have been compared to those of *planetary nebulas* in our galaxy: rapidly expanding shells of gas surrounding hot stars that presumably have undergone a nova explosion recently (see the photograph on page 162).

The dense nuclei of Seyfert galaxies are so bright with turbulent, agitated gases that the glare blots out the spiral arms (Mount Wilson and Palomar Observatories)

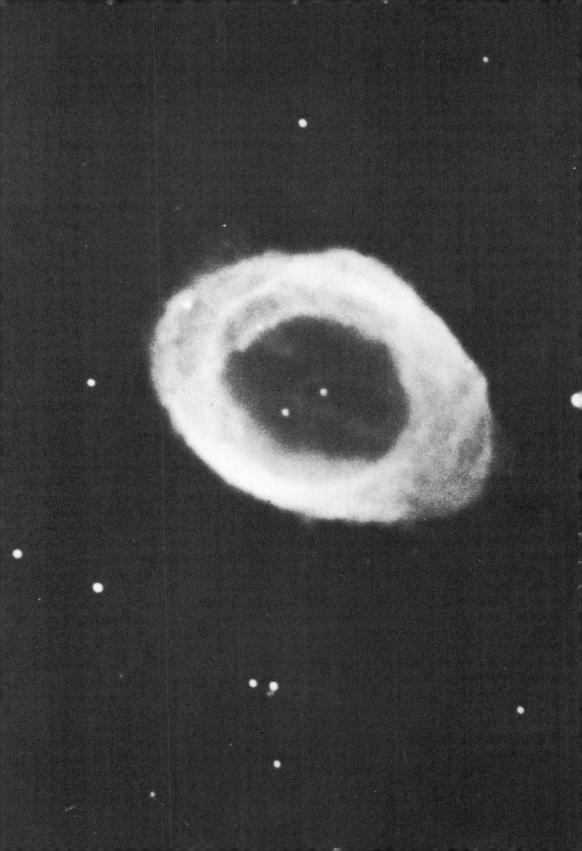

The emission lines in the quasars' spectra have been identified as those caused by perfectly ordinary elements: hydrogen, helium, carbon, neon, magnesium, silicon, sulfur, argon, and iron. Although the elements are highly ionized, they seem to be present in about the same abundances as in ordinary stars and galaxies; the only possible exception to this might be helium, which seems to be less abundant than it is elsewhere. As of this writing, iron is the only element heavier than argon that has been identified in the quasars' spectra. No one can yet say for certain whether the apparent helium deficiency or the scarcity of heavy elements means anything significant.

The emission lines show that the gases have a density of about 10^4 to 10^7 particles per cubic centimeter. This is much rarer than the sun's shining surface layer, the photosphere, where the density is some 10^{16} particles per cubic centimeter. The spectral lines are broad, rather than narrow and sharp, indicating that the gas is in rapid motion. Velocities of 2000 to 3000 km/sec have been estimated. The rapid motion of the gas looks much like the behavior of the gas shell blown outward in a planetary nebula. But for the quasars, there is no sure way of telling whether the gas motion is outward, away from the core, or inward and toward the core. Some theories are based on the idea that the quasars are undergoing gravitational collapse. In that case, the gas motion would be inward.

Some of the quasars show very puzzling absorption spectra. Quasars such as PKS 0327–23 and TON 1530 have between

The Ring Nebula in the constellation Lyra is an example of a planetary nebula, where a star is surrounded by an expanding shell of gases. Spectra of planetary nebulas resemble in some ways the spectra of quasars (Mount Wilson and Palomar Observatories)

twenty-five and fifty absorption lines in their spectra. The red-shifts of these lines are all less than the redshifts of the same quasar, as measured from their emission-line spectra. What's more, even in a single quasar, different absorption lines show different redshifts!

One possible explanation is that the absorption lines are produced by various shells of gases that surround the quasar's central core, and these shells are each moving at a different velocity. On the other hand, some astronomers believe that the absorption is caused by the fact that the light from the quasar is passing through intervening clouds of gases. They theorize that we may be seeing the quasars through very thin "halos" of gases that surround galaxies placed between us and the quasars. The halo gases produce the absorption lines. The various redshifts, then, are characteristic of the absorbing galaxies, not of the quasars themselves.

If this second explanation holds true, it provides strong evidence that the quasars are very distant objects, at least they are beyond the intervening galaxies.

The gas temperatures are around 30,000°K, according to the most widely accepted estimates. But, just as in the case of the sun's corona, this refers more to the kinetic (motion) energy of the particles than to their heat energy.

The central core of a quasar must be a fantastic inferno of energy. Calculations have predicted core temperatures as high as 100,000°K; that is the value for the *surface* of the core, not the interior. The core luminosity may be something like that of a laser—brighter than any star. And the physical processes that are generating the quasar's energy are something we can only guess at.

The structure of the radio and optical spectra both show that nonthermal processes are at work in the outer shell gases of the quasars. The fact that 3C 446's light is polarized adds convincing weight to the idea that the outer portions of the quasars are natural synchrotrons.

We can draw a qualitative picture of a typical quasar, if we keep in mind that all our knowledge about the physical characteristics of the quasars is still tentative.

The core is no larger than 10^{12} kilometers across, and may be more like the size of the solar system. The core consists of 100,000°K gas of tremendous optical brightness. Surrounding this core is a shell, or perhaps several shells, of 30,000°K gases. A magnetic field permeates these outer regions and drives electrons to velocities close to light speed. As the electrons whirl along the magnetic field lines, they emit radio energy.

The gas shells themselves are either being blown outward, possibly by a core explosion, or are falling in toward the core under a process of gravitational collapse.

This picture is hardly more than a sketch. Some of the details are no doubt wrong. The entire picture may be sadly off-target. But, to date, that is what the evidence seems to show.

The sketch above showed, very roughly, the presumed structure of 3C 273. It is interesting to compare a photograph of this quasar (as seen in Chapter 1) with the short-exposure photograph of the core of M 87 (as seen in Chapter 5). The similarities may be entirely coincidental, but they are certainly striking. Both 3C 273 and M 87 are producing radio emission by synchrotron radiation. But while M 87 is shining visually with the light of 1000 billion stars, 3C 273—if it is really 500 megaparsecs or more away—is at least a hundred times brighter.

8

The Quest
Goes On

We dance round in a ring and suppose,
But the Secret sits in the middle and knows.

Robert Frost

THE BEAUTY AND THE POWER AND THE USEFULNESS OF SCIENCE
stems from its ability to answer our questions about the nature
of the physical world. The excitement of science, though,
comes from the unanswered questions—the problems that
still challenge our wit and patience and courage. That is
why the quasars are so exciting: although much has been
learned about them in only a few years, there are no real
answers to basic questions.

How distant are they?

What powers them?

What are they?

Theories there are; plenty of them. But no answers.

The problem of their distance, of course, is crucial to understanding the quasars. If they are cosmologically distant, then

they may very well be powered by some means that is completely beyond the capability of nuclear fusion. Does this mean that there are energy sources, undreamed of here on earth, that man might someday tap for his own purposes?

Where do the quasars fit into the plan of the universe? Are they new galaxies being born? Old galaxies exploding? Fragments blown away from galaxies? Superlarge stars?

LOCAL OR COSMOLOGICAL?

When it was first discovered that the quasars show large redshifts, most astronomers immediately assumed that this meant they were partaking of the general expansion of the universe, as the farther galaxies are assumed to be doing. Thus, the larger the redshift, the farther the quasar. Quasars with redshifts of more than 200 percent are reasoned to be traveling at better than 80 percent of light speed and thus are believed to be in the neighborhood of 3000 megaparsecs away—practically at the "curtain of light."

But if the quasars are that distant, their energy outputs are beyond anything else known in the universe. And their brightness fluctuations lead to the suspicion that most of this energy is being emitted from a small region of each quasar. The explanation of how this energy can be generated in such a huge amount from such a small core has stumped the astrophysicists. Several possibilities have been suggested, but all of them fall short of explaining what is observed.

This has led several workers to consider two alternatives to the "cosmological" idea, both of which picture the quasars as relatively nearby: between 10 and 100 megaparsecs. One possibility is that the redshifts are not Doppler shifts at all, but are caused by gravitational contraction. The other "local" alternative is that the quasars are objects that have been shot out of nearby galaxies—or perhaps out of our own Milky Way—at high speeds.

The idea of a gravitational redshift is based firmly on known physical facts. A strong gravitational field will shift the wavelengths of light coming out of the star (or galaxy or quasar) toward the red. The effect is exactly the same as the Doppler effect, as far as what we would see is concerned. Light waves coming from the sun are redshifted by a minute amount. But to produce redshifts of the sizes observed in the quasars, titanic gravitational fields would be needed. This in turn means that the quasars would have to be supermassive objects, perhaps 10^8 times the mass of the sun. While enormous by solar standards, this is still about 1000 times less massive than a typical spiral galaxy.

Thus the quasars might be "superstars," of a size and mass intermediate between a star and a galaxy. They must be about 10 megaparsecs away, at least, or else we would feel the effects of their gravitational fields here in the Milky Way.

What of the idea that the quasars are objects that were ejected from galaxies? Galaxies sometimes explode; perhaps even our Milky Way exploded about a million years ago. That could explain the radio halo around our galaxy; it might even explain the quasars.

If the quasars are local objects, their energy outputs drop by a factor of 10^4 from their "cosmological" outputs, as Table 13 showed. Thus they might be something akin to the nuclei of Seyfert or other types of radio galaxies. Alternatively, if they are slightly less massive (say, about 10^6–10^7 solar masses) they might even be something like globular star clusters. Globular clusters have been observed out as far as 80,000 parsecs from the Milky Way; perhaps they, too, have been shot out of the galaxy.

In general, the local theories make it easier to account for the energy requirements of the quasars. But another problem arises: what can produce the energy of a galactic explosion strong enough to hurl dozens, perhaps hundreds, of quasars outward with such enormous velocities? Calculations have shown that a galactic explosion of such violence would expend just about the same amount of energy that a "cosmological" quasar is estimated to be putting out. And so the energy problem remains with us.

Moreover, if the quasars were ejected from nearby galaxies, why don't we see any approaching us? Why are they all running away? Why are there no blueshifts among the redshifts?

There are two possible answers. First, perhaps they were ejected from the Milky Way itself, or from a galaxy (or galaxies) so close by that the quasars have all gone past us and are now receding into the depths of intergalactic space. Admittedly, that means that our own and the nearby galaxies would be different from all the other galaxies. Can we safely assume that the quasars have been ejected *only* from galaxies close enough to make blueshifts unlikely? Probably not.

The second answer may be better: it might be very difficult to detect a blueshifted quasar from the surface of the earth. The light from such an approaching quasar would have started out in the infrared wavelengths and been blueshifted into the visible region. Visible wavelengths would be blueshifted into the ultraviolet region of the spectrum, which is blocked from us by the earth's upper atmosphere. The quasar's ultraviolet radiation would be shifted down toward the x-ray region, which is also blocked by the upper atmosphere. The light we would see, then, would have originated as infrared.

There are very few strong spectral lines in the infrared that could be clearly identified as such if they showed up on visible spectrograms. Many suspected quasars have been observed that show very faint or absolutely no spectral lines at all. Are they blueshifted?

And consider the radio frequencies. A blueshifted quasar would be emitting radio energy at extremely high frequencies, probably higher than any present radio telescopes are equipped to receive. Are the so-called "radio-quiet" quasars actually blueshifted objects emitting at these high frequencies?

Spectrographic equipment above most or all of the earth's atmosphere (in a high-altitude balloon or rocket, or in orbit or on the moon) should be able to search for blueshifted quasars in the far ultraviolet and x-ray regions of the spectrum, where they would be more likely to be detected. Interestingly, several x-ray sources have been found by rocket-borne equipment, but these are not thought to be connected to the quasars in any way.

The entire argument of local versus cosmological quasars has strong emotional overtones.

If the quasars are local, then here is a startling case of the redshift having nothing at all to do with the expansion of the universe. What about the normal galaxies, then? Are their redshifts really due to the expansion of the universe? Is the universe really expanding? The whole cornerstone of modern cosmology would come under some suspicion if the quasars are proved to be local. On the other hand, the Steady-State theory may be enhanced if the quasars are not cosmological.

Finally, if the quasars are local objects, some of the glamour goes out of them. They are not the most distant objects yet discovered. They are not possible "eye witnesses" of the Big Bang itself (if there was one). They are still very unusual, highly intriguing objects that may eventually tell us much about the nature of galaxies and answer some basic questions of astrophysics. But some of the emotional impact will be missing. And no matter how impersonal scientists may try to be about their work, they are influenced by their emotions.

It is no surprise, then, to find some of the top Steady-State people working hard to prove that the quasars are local, and some of those who have argued strongest against the Steady-State theory working equally hard to show that they are cosmological.

What do the observations show? Hoyle and others have pointed out that if the apparent magnitudes (either optical or radio) of the quasars are plotted against their redshifts, there is no correlation at all. Unlike the magnitude versus redshift plot for the galaxies, where Hubble's Law becomes apparent, there seems to be very little relationship between a quasar's brightness and its redshift. This may be a powerful argument in favor of the idea that the redshifts have nothing to do with a quasar's distance. After all, the farther a quasar, the dimmer it should be. If an increasing redshift means an increasing distance, then the largest redshifts should be matched with the dimmest quasars. But they are not.

Of course, this argument assumes that the quasars are all —on the average, at least—of pretty much the same intrinsic luminosity. Knowing as little as we do about the quasars, this assumption may be unfounded.

To prove the local theory, it will probably be necessary either to find a blueshifted quasar, or to spot a proper motion in a quasar. By combining the quasar's redshift and its proper motion, it should be possible to determine its distance. It is unlikely that any quasar farther than 10 megaparsecs would show any detectable proper motion. Such a discovery, then, would clinch the "local" hypothesis.

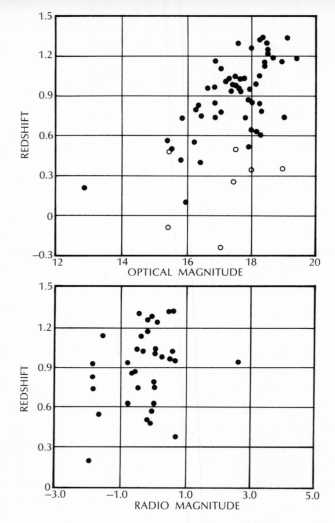

Figure 21. These plots of quasar redshifts versus optical magnitude (above) and radio magnitude (below) reveal no discernible relationship between a quasar's redshift and its brightness. For normal galaxies, such plots result in the straight-line Hubble relationship shown in Figure 14 (after Hoyle)

BEYOND THERMONUCLEAR POWER?

Perhaps the most far-reaching problem associated with the quasars is the question of their source of energy. Thermonuclear fusion—which powers the sun and man's most destructive weapon—may not be energetic enough to account for the quasars' outpouring of light and radio waves, *even if the quasars are local objects.*

To review the energy requirements, see Table 13. The optical and radio outputs of normal galaxies, radio galaxies, and quasars were given there, with the power expressed in kilowatts. Since we are now going to be discussing both energy and power, we will speak of energy in units of ergs and of power in units of ergs per second. For purposes of comparison, 10^{10} ergs/sec equals 1 kw.

Radio galaxies are emitting as much as 10^{45} ergs/sec. Quasars, if they are at cosmological distances, are emitting as much in the radio wavelengths, and ten times more (10^{46} ergs/sec) in optical wavelengths. If we assume that these power levels have been maintained for a million years in each case (10^{13} seconds), then we find that the total amount of energy radiated by a radio galaxy over that time is 10^{58} ergs; for a quasar, it is 10^{59} ergs.

While it is likely that the radio galaxies have "been in business" for more than a million years, it might well be that the quasars are much shorter lived. At any rate, a million years is a good period of time for the sake of comparing the two types of objects.

Both types of objects are apparently powered, at least in part, by synchrotron processes. Physicists know that these processes are notoriously inefficient. Therefore, they reason that a radio galaxy or quasar must have a considerably higher amount of energy stored up inside itself than its emission power would at first indicate. For example, if we assume that the synchrotron processes are about 1 percent efficient, then the total energy in a radio galaxy or quasar must be one hundred times greater than the energy emitted. Thus, over a million-year period, we need 10^{60} ergs to account for the energy emission from a radio galaxy, and 10^{61} ergs for a quasar. Some astrophysicists feel that the synchrotron efficiencies might be even lower, so that the quasars may have even more stored energy.

For both the radio galaxies and the quasars, the method by which this stored energy is transferred into synchrotron radiation is not clearly understood. Neither is there firm understanding of exactly how the energy is stored: In the object's magnetic field? In the particles of the gas clouds? In stars? The quasars might not contain stars, although they probably have rather strong magnetic fields and certainly much free gas.

To make these gigantic numbers more concrete, consider the total amount of energy in the sun. Not the energy that the sun beams out, the 0.7 percent of its matter that is transformed into sunlight by thermonuclear fusion, but the entire amount of energy that would be liberated if *all* the sun's mass were converted to energy in accordance with Einstein's $E = mc^2$. The sun's mass is roughly 2×10^{33} grams. The velocity of light, c, is 3×10^{10} cm/sec. In this formula, c^2 is equivalent to the number of ergs per gram of matter; therefore we have $(3 \times 10^{10})^2$ or very nearly 10^{21} ergs/gram. The total energy locked up in the sun's mass, then, is about 2×10^{54} ergs.

A typical quasar, with 10^{61} ergs of energy stored in it, contains as much energy as ten million stars—that is, the *total conversion* of ten million stars' mass into energy.

If the quasars are local objects and their energy levels are some ten thousand times lower, they contain the energy of "only" a thousand stars, or ten thousand, at most. Globular star clusters have millions of stars in them, although they are not converting each star completely into energy. If the quasars have been ejected by nearby galaxies, then the galaxies in question must have generated something like 10^{60} ergs or more, to get the quasars up to their enormous velocities. Where did *that* come from?

And again, if the quasars are cosmological objects, shining with the energy of the complete conversion of ten million stars' mass, how do they pack a large fraction of that energy into a region only slightly larger than the solar system? And where does the energy come from?

A number of proposals have been put forward to account for the energy production in the quasars. They include: (1) gravitational energy; (2) supernova chain explosions; (3) stellar collisions; and (4) matter-antimatter annihilation.

Gravitational Energy. When the quasars were first discovered, one suggested explanation for their redshifts and their energy source was that they are massive superstars, perhaps ten million times as massive as the sun.

The observed energy output of the quasars would then come from gravitational contraction, as the quasar slowly squeezes in on itself. In the early stages of a star's evolution, it begins to shine from gravitational energy released as it contracts from protostar to main sequence star. If a "superstar" of 10^8 solar masses undergoes gravitational contraction, its light output would be equivalent to that of the quasars.

Moreover, the enormous gravitational field of such a massive object would redshift the light waves leaving the object. The quasars' redshifts would not be Doppler ones, but ones caused by gravity. The quasars therefore would not be cosmological objects, but local—about ten megaparsecs away. If they were closer than that, their immense gravitational fields would be detectable in the Milky Way.

But there are serious problems with this superstar concept. For one thing, although the redshifts of the quasars vary from 0.13 percent to 222 percent, their energy outputs are all estimated to be close to the 10^{60}–10^{62} ergs value. If gravity is responsible for the different redshifts, it would seem that there must be large differences in mass (and therefore in gravitational field strength) from one quasar to another. But if gravity is also responsible for the energy output—which appears similar from one quasar to another—the masses should be similar, too. Can these two contradictory possibilities be reconciled into a single consistent theory?

Another problem is that a superstar of 10^8 solar masses would probably break up into smaller objects; calculations have shown that a single such massive object would be structurally unstable. The superstar theory backers answer this in two ways: first, they have shown that the superstar might not break up if it is rotating; second, they claim that even if it does break up, it can still be treated as a single object, consisting of many parts, of 10^8 solar masses.

If the quasars are superstars that are contracting, they may well be on a one-way ride to oblivion. Studies of gravitational contraction have shown that when a massive body contracts, it may reach a critical size and density where the gravitational field becomes so powerful that it overcomes all other forces and pulls the body in on itself until the body literally disappears!

The body becomes so small and dense, and its gravitational field so strong, that not even light waves can escape its surface. The body cannot be seen; only its gravitational field can be detected. In a sense, the body has left our universe; it has dug a hole, jumped in, and pulled the hole in after itself. Such a case is called a *Schwarzschild singularity*, after the German physicist Karl Schwarzschild (1873–1916), who first showed that such a phenomenon can happen.

It may be, though, that the quasars are massive superstars that are not contracting but are lit by perfectly ordinary thermonuclear energy. William A. Fowler (born 1911) of the California Institute of Technology points out that a body of some 10^8 solar masses could produce 10^{60} ergs over a million years by hydrogen fusion. If the quasars are fusion-powered superstars, presumably their redshifts are Doppler shifts, and they are at cosmological distances.

The reason astrophysicists and cosmologists have invoked superstars is twofold: to explain the observed redshifts of the quasars as gravitational shifts instead of Doppler shifts; and to provide a gravitational (or, following Fowler, thermonuclear) explanation for the observed energy outputs of the quasars. The superstars are considered to be "local" objects, although they cannot be any closer than ten megaparsecs for reasons stated earlier.

Some astrophysicists, however, have pointed out that the immense gravitational fields postulated by the superstar theory would prevent the quasars from giving off the emission lines that have been observed in their spectra. Also, they believe that the gravitational contraction would go quickly to its conclusion—perhaps to a Schwarzschild singularity—and our chances of catching a quasar before it disappeared would be slim. Finally they argue that gravitational contraction would produce quasars of much higher density than the observations show. Since the quasars do give off emission lines, since there are hundreds of them in view, and since their outer shells seem much rarer than the densities called for by the gravitational contraction concept, most cosmologists have not accepted the superstar idea.

Stellar Explosions. Suppose that the quasars are cosmological objects, with Doppler redshifts. Suppose further that they are the size of a galaxy, with cores considerably larger than the light fluctuations would indicate.

If the quasars are something like a distant galaxy, then

their cores may well be rich with stars. If the quasars are young objects, as most cosmologists believe they are, the star-thick cores may contain young, massive blue giants and super-giant stars. Such stars evolve quickly and end their brief, brilliant lives as supernovas.

Some theorists have considered that if the stars in the core of a quasar are packed closely enough, a supernova of one star could trigger a chain of such explosions in its neighboring stars. Perhaps the entire core would flash into an enormous series of supernovas. Thus, the intensely bright core of a quasar—with sudden changes in brightness—may really be a string of supernova explosions.

An alternative theory to the supernova-chain idea is that the stars in a thickly packed quasar core might be colliding with each other. The effect is much the same as the supernova theory—enormous energies are released for each such violent encounter.

A typical supernova emits as much as 10^{51} ergs—about a billion years' worth of normal energy output for a sunlike star. Since a quasar gives off at least 10^{60} ergs over a million years, it would take a billion stars (or supernovas) to power a single quasar.

Even if the quasars are farther away than any other object, they are comparatively small objects, smaller than most galaxies. And their cores are small, so small that it is difficult to see how a billion stars fit into them. There is no evidence that the quasars contain any stars at all.

Antimatter. The annihilation of matter and antimatter certainly provides enough energy to account for the observed performances of the quasars. But antimatter reactions yield gamma radiation mostly, not visible light. This is a principal objection to the antimatter explanation.

The thermonuclear reactions, however, that power the sun

produce mainly gamma radiation, too. The gamma-wave-length energy is gradually shifted to visible wavelengths as the light waves make their way from the core of the sun to the surface. Could something like this be happening in the quasars? An antimatter reaction could produce gamma radiation at the core of the quasar. The core is surrounded by shells of gas. Might the gamma waves be shifted to visible (or ultraviolet) light as they work their way through these outer shells of gas?

The problem this raises, though, is even tougher: How can antimatter exist in the core of the quasar and not outside?

And, since proton-antiproton reactions give rise to radio emission as well as gamma rays and electron-positron pairs, the antimatter theory might account for the radio emission from quasars quite handily.

All of these are merely ideas. None of them explains the detailed behavior of the quasars. It is possible, perhaps even likely, that the real explanation for the quasars' energy has not been dreamed of yet and is sitting like Frost's secret in the midst of all the theories.

THE BEGINNING OR THE END?

Astronomers still have no satisfactory explanation for the energy sources that produce the radio emissions in the strong radio galaxies. And if the quasars are local objects, then we must find some 10^{60} ergs of explosive energy inside normal-looking and radio galaxies.

Just where do the quasars fit? Modern astronomical and cosmological thought can build up a smooth progression of ideas: clouds of gas and dust form stars, stars make up galaxies, galaxies are grouped into clusters, and clusters march on toward the edge of the observable universe. The quasars jolt this well-oiled sequence. And that's all to the good. When ideas become too comfortable, they've generally outlived their usefulness.

The problem of the quasars may play an important role in another thorny problem facing cosmologists: explaining the origin of the galaxies. There are no satisfactory theories to account for the formation of galaxies. How do they come into existence? Why do galaxies never get bigger than the E0 types? What makes one galaxy a spiral and another an elliptical? Are all the galaxies of the same age?

To this list we can add another question: what is the relationship between the quasars and the galaxies?

If the quasars are cosmologically distant, then they may be new galaxies in the process of formation. According to the Big Bang theory, galaxy formation was going on some ten billion years ago, and it should be observable now.

If the quasars are local objects, they might be the results of galactic explosions. Do such explosions herald the death agonies of a galaxy, just as nova or supernova explosions mark the final stages of a star's lifetime?

Schematic drawings of different types of radio galaxies appeared in Chapter 5. Now, in the accompanying drawing, these radio galaxies are arranged into a sequence, and the quasars and the M 82-type exploding galaxies are added to show a pattern, from quasar to Cygnus A-type radio galaxy, of the history of an explosion in the core of a galaxy. This pattern may be completely artificial, created by the selection and arrangement of subject matter. But the scheme brings up interesting possibilities, nevertheless. It could mean that, even if the quasars are cosmologically distant, they are caused by—in fact they are the first stages of—explosions in the cores of galaxies.

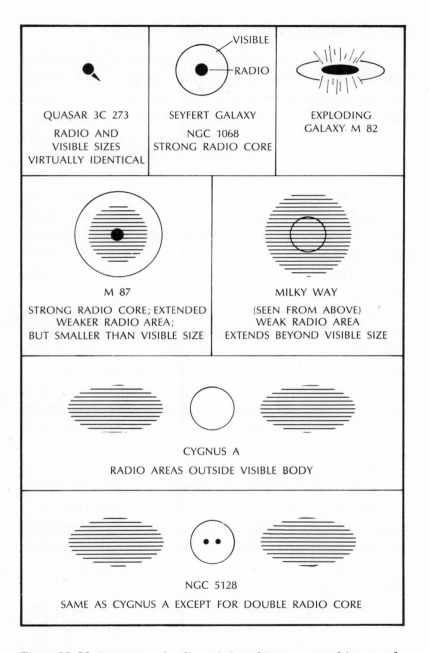

Figure 22. Various types of radio-emitting objects, arranged in a purely hypothetical sequence. Could there be such a straightforward relationship among the different radio sources?

Alfven goes a step further. He has proposed the idea that when galaxies are created, they contain roughly equal amounts of ordinary matter and antimatter. The two types of matter are most likely to meet in the densest part of a galaxy—that is, in the galactic core. The annihilation of matter and anti-matter, then, is the driving energy source for explosions in the cores of galaxies. Alfven suggests that the quasars are the first steps in this process, galaxies where the explosion has recently begun. In Alfven's view, the quasars are cosmologically distant. In later stages of this antimatter-driven core explosion, the galaxy becomes what we call a Seyfert galaxy, then a strong radio galaxy, and finally an ordinary galaxy such as the Milky Way.

Could the quasars be the bright cores of whole galaxies, cores that are in the first stages of exploding? Like the much-closer Seyfert galaxies (which the quasars resemble in some ways), these cores would far outshine the outer portions of the galaxy. If the objects are 1000 megaparsecs or more away, we would not expect to be able to see the outer parts of the galaxy—only the intensely bright cores would be visible.

On the other hand, consider the case for "local" quasars.

There is ample evidence that galaxies explode. M 82, the Seyfert galaxies, the radio galaxies, even our own Milky Way provide evidence of explosions. Estimates of the energy stored in powerful radio galaxies work out to 10^{60} ergs—which is about the energy necessary for a galactic explosion that would hurl out local quasars.

Could the quasars be something like the size and mass of globular star clusters? Could they have been ejected from nearby galaxies by core explosions? Might they have come from the Milky Way itself?

If the quasars were blasted out of the Milky Way, it would explain why no blueshifted objects have been seen and why the quasars seem to be clustered more or less around the galaxies' poles. Studies of M 82 and of the Milky Way's probable magnetic field structure show that, if our galaxy exploded, the "debris" might well be hurled poleward, rather than out along the equator (see Figure 23).

But it is unlikely that the Milky Way, alone of all the galaxies, should have been parent to all the quasars. There is evidence to indicate that many quasars lie close to radio galaxies and peculiar galaxies (that is, lie close to them in the sense of angular separation as seen from earth; whether the quasars are actually a relatively short distance from such

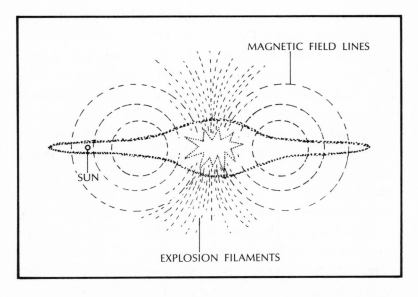

Figure 23. If an explosion occurred in the core of the Milky Way galaxy, the galaxy's magnetic field might tend to shelter the solar system. Filaments of hot gases, hurled outward by the explosion, would probably travel along magnetic field lines, rather than across them. Thus most of the expelled gas would head away from the galaxy

galaxies remains a wide-open question). Perhaps the quasars have been ejected from these galaxies.

Steady-State theorists have wrestled with two other intriguing possibilities. Some have considered that the quasars represent matter expelled from a galaxy; others are examining the possibility that the quasars are the "little bangs" of new matter coming into existence in intergalactic space.

The first idea is based on the assumption that matter is continuously created inside of existing galaxies. But galaxies can attain only a certain maximum size; observations have shown that no spirals are much bigger than the Milky Way, and no ellipticals larger than the giant E0 types. No one knows why this is so. The theorists put together the assumption and the observation, and they reason that the quasars are chunks of matter hurled out of galaxies because the galaxies have reached their maximum "allowable" size, and new matter is still being created inside them.

Other Steady-State enthusiasts take the opposite tack. They stick to the idea that new matter enters the universe only in empty space, in between the galaxies. But perhaps the introduction of new matter is somehow influenced by the presence of a galaxy nearby. Thus the quasars may be the sudden "popping-in" of new matter, rather close by an existing galaxy.

The theories march on: the quasars represent events that happened close to the time of original Big Bang; they represent evidence of the continuous creation of new matter in a Steady-State universe; they are something like galaxies; they are something like globular star clusters; they mark the birth of a new galaxy; they prove that old galaxies explode . . . and so forth, with many variations and little verification from actual observed phenomena.

THE CONTINUING QUEST

So the search goes on, both for new observational data from the quasars themselves and for new ideas that can help to explain what they are.

The biggest achievement through observation would be, of course, a clear distance measurement from the earth to even one quasar. The detection of a blueshifted quasar, or proper motion in a quasar, would also serve to pin down the local versus cosmological controversy. If distances can be established, then the *real* work of understanding the quasars can begin: the unraveling of the secrets of their energy source, the reasons for their puzzling fluctuations, their relationship to galaxies (if any), and their place in cosmology.

If there are more questions than answers in this book, it is because the challenge of the quasars is still practically new, and little is known compared to what needs to be learned. True, many details have been left out and many complex problems oversimplified in the effort to present a feeling for the outlines of the quasar problem and to inspire interest enough to read further on the quasars and allied subjects.

One thing is certain. Events are moving swiftly, so swiftly that much of what has been said here may be obsolete by the time you read it. At least one rocket experiment has detected an x-ray source near—or maybe in—3C 273. Radio telescopes are studying the pulsars, which are probably neutron stars that may be heading down that one-way chute of gravitational collapse that ends in a Schwarzschild singularity. Big new telescopes—optical and radio—are being built. And electronic boosters for optical telescopes are starting to improve our visual view of the heavens. Also, plans are under way for mounting both kinds of telescopes in satellites so that we may see the heavens without earth's foggy blanket of air in the way.

Astronomy is in ferment as new discoveries and new theories challenge our ideas about the basic nature of the universe. The quasars may hold the key to some of the basic puzzles of cosmology: Is the universe truly expanding? What is the energy source for galactic explosions? Do we live in an evolving or steady-state universe?

These questions are so big that you might wonder if they matter at all, one way or the other, to the average person. Perhaps they do not. And yet, man has always searched the skies, seeking to understand the world in which he finds himself. For as long as recorded history he has been wondering about the nature of the universe.

Each gain in knowledge, each question answered, has led him to ask bigger, tougher questions. The quasars present a host of new questions. Finding the answers will be exciting. And the new questions that follow those answers will be even more so.

A Quasar Chronology

1959   Third Cambridge Catalogue (3C) of strong radio sources is published.

1960   Radio astronomy groups in England, Australia, Russia, the United States, and elsewhere work to fix precise locations of radio sources. Astronomers hope to find "radio stars."

Thomas Matthews (California Institute of Technology Radio Observatory) and Allan R. Sandage (Mt. Wilson and Palomar Observatories, California Institute of Technology) find blue "stars" coinciding with the positions of several radio sources.

Sandage, using the Mt. Palomar 200-inch telescope, finds nebulosity around 3C 48; spectra for 3C 48 are obtained, but no identification of spectral lines can be made. 3C 48 is believed to be a "radio star."

1963   Cyril Hazard and his colleagues (University of Sydney) use lunar occultation technique to fix positions of several radio sources; they find 3C 273 to be a double object.

Maarten Schmidt (Mt. Wilson and Palomar) locates 3C 273 with the 200-inch telescope and finds it has two optical components; spectra for 3C 273 are obtained. Schmidt deduces that 3C 273 spectrum is redshifted 16 percent.

Jesse L. Greenstein (Mt. Wilson and Palomar) and Matthews measure 36 percent redshift for 3C 48.

Many additional quasars are found. Most astronomers agree that redshifts mean they are "cosmologically" distant (billions of light years from earth).

William A. Fowler (California Institute of Technology) and Fred Hoyle (Cambridge University) suggest that quasars may be supermassive objects, and redshifts may be gravitational in origin; if so, redshifts are of no use in determining distances of quasars.

1964   James Terrell (Los Alamos Scientific Laboratory, University of California) suggests that quasars may be "local" objects, ejected at high speeds from Milky Way galaxy.

C. R. Lynds (Lick Observatory) and Sandage announce that irregular galaxy M 82 is exploding.

1965   Sandage suggests that "radio quiet" quasars may greatly outnumber quasars that are strong radio sources.

1966   Hoyle and Geoffrey Burbidge (University of California, La Jolla) suggest that quasars may be objects ejected by "relatively nearby" (around 30-300 million light years distant) radio galaxies.

Halton C. Arp (Mt. Wilson and Palomar) suggests quasars are associated with peculiar galaxies.

Quasars with redshifts exceeding 200 percent are found; these redshifts correspond to a recession velocity of 80 percent of the speed of light, or more.

Peter Strittmatter and John Faulkner (Cambridge University) and Malcolm Walmsley (University of California, La Jolla) show that quasars are apparently clustered more closely at the Milky Way's poles than near the equator.

For Further Reading

While most of the technical papers about the quasars are in the professional journals of astronomy and physics, articles written for the general reader often appear in the British weekly *Nature*, in *Science* (published weekly by the American Association for the Advancement of Science), and in the monthly *Scientific American*.

Below are some of the articles and books that contain more information about the quasars and related topics.

George Abell, *Exploration of the Universe*, Holt, Rinehart and Winston, New York, 1964. A comprehensive review of practically every facet of astronomy, up to (but unfortunately not including) the quasars.

Hannes Alfvèn, "Antimatter and Cosmology," *Scientific American*, Vol. 216, No. 4, April 1967 (pp. 106–14).

Hannes Alfvèn, *Worlds-Antiworlds: Antimatter in Cosmology*, W. H. Freeman & Co., San Francisco, 1966. These two writings explore the question of antimatter in cosmology; the book also describes the basics of plasma physics, which is Alfvèn's specialty.

Hannes Alfvèn and Aina Elvius, "Antimatter, Quasi-stellar Objects, and the Evolution of Galaxies," *Science*, Vol. 164, Number 3882, May 23, 1969 (pp. 911–917).

Halton C. Arp, "The Evolution of Galaxies," *Scientific American*, Vol. 208, No. 1, January 1963 (pp. 70–84). A review of the various types of galaxies and some thoughts on their origins.

Ben Bova, *The Milky Way Galaxy*, Holt, Rinehart and Winston, New York, 1961. A somewhat dated but still valuable review for the general reader of stellar astronomy, astrophysics, and astronomical methods.

Geoffrey and Margaret Burbidge, *Quasi-Stellar Objects*, W. H. Freeman & Co., San Francisco, 1967. This Herculean feat of compiling, digesting, and presenting all the pertinent technical literature about the quasars up to early 1967 is excellent but difficult reading.

Geoffrey Burbidge and Fred Hoyle, "The Problem of the Quasi-Stellar Objects," *Scientific American*, Vol. 215, No. 6, December 1966 (pp. 40–52). A clear argument in favor of the "local" hypothesis for the quasars.

Geoffrey R. Burbidge, E. Margaret Burbidge, and Allan R. Sandage,

"Evidence for the Occurrence of Violent Events in the Nuclei of Galaxies," *Reviews of Modern Physics*, Vol. 35, No. 4, October 1963 (pp. 947–72). This paper examines all the evidence for galactic explosions, including the quasars.

Hong-Yee Chiu, "Gravitational Collapse," *Physics Today*, Vol. 17, No. 5, May 1964 (pp. 21–34). A well-written summary of the observations and theories about the quasars as of late 1963.

R. W. Clarke, "Locating Radio Sources with the Moon," *Scientific American*, Vol. 214, No. 6, June 1966 (pp. 30–41). The story of using lunar occultations to fix the locations and sizes of the quasars and other radio sources.

James A. Coleman, *Modern Theories of the Universe*, New American Library (Signet Science Library Book), New York, 1963. Historical perspective on cosmological thinking.

Gérard de Vaucouleurs, *Discovery of the Universe*, Macmillan Co., New York, 1957. Valuable historical treatment of the development of astronomical knowledge.

William A. Fowler, *Nuclear Astrophysics*, American Philosophical Society, Philadelphia, 1967. Based on popular lectures, this little gem of a book is filled with lucid information and quiet wit.

George Gamow, *The Creation of the Universe*, Viking Press, New York, 1955. The story of the Big Bang by its best-known and clearest expositor.

Jesse L. Greenstein, "Quasi-Stellar Radio Sources," *Scientific American*, Vol. 209, No. 6, December 1963 (pp. 54–62). A review of the discovery and early observations of the quasars.

D. S. Heeschen, "Radio Galaxies," *Scientific American*, Vol. 206, No. 3, March 1962 (pp. 41–49). A radio astronomer's look at the universe, written before the recognition of the quasars.

Fred Hoyle, *Galaxies, Nuclei and Quasars*, Harper & Row, New York, 1965. The man who's written the most readable explanations of the Steady-State theory examines the effect of the quasars on Steady-State cosmology.

Fred Hoyle, "Recent Developments in Cosmology," *Nature*, Vol. 208, No. 5006, October 9, 1965 (pp. 111–14). A summary of the cosmological implications of the quasars.

F. D. Kahn and H. P. Palmer, *Quasars*, Harvard University Press, Cambridge, 1967. Based on a series of popular lectures, this book gives a thumbnail review of what is known about the quasars.

Robert P. Kraft, "Exploding Stars," *Scientific American*, Vol. 206, No. 4, April 1962 (pp. 56–63). A review of observations and theories about novas and supernovas.

Martha and William Liller, "Planetary Nebulae," *Scientific American*, Vol. 208, No. 4, April 1963 (pp. 60–67). Since the quasars in some ways resemble planetary nebulas, this article is valuable for its discussion of such objects, which are thought to be the remains of exploded stars.

Sir Bernard Lovell, *Our Present Knowledge of the Universe*, Harvard University Press, Cambridge, 1967. This slim volume sketches the contributions of radio astronomy to knowledge of the solar system, our galaxy, and the universe.

Stephen P. Maran and A. G. W. Cameron, "Relativistic Astrophysics," *Science*, Vol. 157, No. 3796, September 29, 1967 (pp. 1517–24). Despite its imposing title, this article deals clearly with quasars, cosmic rays, x-ray sources, and recent discoveries.

Patrick Moore, "The Queer Cosmos," *Science and Technology*, No. 71, November 1967 (pp. 28–37). One of the most popular writers on astronomy discusses the quasars and other recent puzzles.

P. J. E. Peebles and David T. Wilkinson, "The Primeval Fireball," *Scientific American*, Vol. 216, No. 6, June 1967 (pp. 28–37). An account of the discovery and implications of the first new major observational contribution to cosmology since Hubble's redshift announcement in 1929.

Allan R. Sandage, "Exploding Galaxies," *Scientific American*, Vol. 211, No. 5, November 1964 (pp. 38–47). The story of the discovery of the explosion in the M 82 galaxy.

Allan R. Sandage, "The Red-Shift," *Scientific American*, Vol. 198, No. 3, September 1956 (pp. 171–82). A clear description of the redshift measurements and their meaning for cosmology.

Harlow Shapley, *The View from a Distant Star*, Basic Books, Inc., New York, 1963. Science and philosophy by the man who determined the sun's position in the Milky Way. Although the book does not discuss the quasars, it is delightful and thought-provoking.

Robert Silverberg, *Niels Bohr, the Man Who Mapped the Atom*, Macrae Smith Co., Philadelphia, 1965. In addition to a biography of Bohr, the author provides the story of the development of nuclear physics.

Otto Struve, *The Universe*, MIT Press, Cambridge, 1962. Based on a series of lectures, one of the world's greatest astronomers reviews the challenges and rewards of his science.

Kip S. Thorne, "Gravitational Collapse," *Scientific American*, Vol. 217, No. 5, November 1967 (pp. 88–98). An excursion into the weird world of superdense matter and disappearing stars.

Ray J. Weymann, "Seyfert Galaxies," *Scientific American*, Vol. 220, No. 1, January 1969 (pp. 28–37). An up-to-date review of the unusual Seyfert galaxies, showing how they compare to the quasars.

Index

DATE DUE